Tom Slemen
HAUNTED
LIVERPOOL 13

The Bluecoat Press

CONTENTS

INTRODUCTION

Welcome to the thirteenth volume of *Haunted Liverpool*, a series of books that delves, not only into local paranormal occurrences from the past and present, but also into unusual incidents that have taken place in an around the city. Liverpool is certainly a city which harbours a wealth of unusual stories, and a lot of them are still waiting to be told, but I am trying to rectify the situation by uncovering new stories each and every day. I get tip-offs by email, snail-mail and often by telephone about these untapped mines of fascinating history.

For example, many people have contacted me over the years about a certain house in St John's Road, Bootle, which is apparently haunted by a grotesque-looking, inhuman apparition. Just the other day I received a letter from a Mrs Preston of Wallasey, who once lived with her mother Ada and grandmother, in a certain house on St John's Road in 1918. I immediately wondered if it was the particular house I had heard so much about.

The house had a large cellar, one part of which was for coal, and the other part was whitewashed and used for drying laundry on clothes maidens. The adults decided that it would be an ideal place for the children to play when it was too wet or cold outside. The writer of the letter described how, shortly after they had moved in, something terrible happened in that cellar to make them think again ...

... My grandma asked my mother to take the little ones to play in the cellar while she did some work with the older children. Everyone had a job to do and all was going well. Charlie and Bess could be heard squealing with laughter as they played hide and seek, when suddenly, Charlie screamed and poor Bess was struck dumb. Bess shook with fight and pointed to an horrific gargoyle face coming through the wall. It started to clank its chains and made a grab at Charlie. My mother ran down to the cellar and grabbed the two little ones and dragged them up the cellar steps as fast as possible. They clung to her, as she banged the cellar door shut and would not let go. They refused to go down to the cellar again, until it had been exorcised.

That 'gargoyle' has been seen by subsequent occupiers of that house and other neighbouring houses in St John's Road, but who or what it is that is doing the haunting is anybody's guess, but I aim to find out. Research will have to be undertaken, censuses consulted, and newspaper archives read by the acre. A sizeable part of these investigations is carried out by my diligent researcher Kevin Roach, at the Central Library in Liverpool, a place I would advise all budding ghost investigators and family tree enthusiasts to check out, for it has first rate facilities for delving into local history.

There are plenty of other mysterious old stories which I am trying to get to the bottom of. For example, in the Victorian publication, *Annals of Electricity*, there is an account of something which took place in Liverpool on 11 May 1842 which has no rational explanation. The gist of the story is that some clothes hanging on a washing line suddenly shot upwards into the sky on a beautiful summer's day. They hung in the hair for a while, then moved slowly away. Smoke from nearby chimneys indicated that above the ground there was a gentle southward wind, but the clothes moved across the clear blue sky towards the north, until they were lost to sight.

Then there is the vague but spooky tale concerning Number 203 Edge Lane, at the corner of Holt Road. It is a beautiful house with an interesting turret. Over the years, a few strange tales about the upper room within that turret have come to my attention. In the 1930s a young couple lived there, as lodgers I believe, and both died within months of one another. It was said that on certain nights, the music of a gramophone player could be heard up in that turret, and that the silhouettes of the two lovers could be glimpsed on the tussore curtains of the room where they had lived, clinging to each other as they danced to a gramophone playing Cole Porter's 'I Get A Kick Out Of You'. After nightfall, on the Holt Road of long ago, people would scuttle past that turret for fear of seeing the ghosts at the window.

How did the lovers die? Well, legend has it that they were cursed to death after opening the dreaded 'Blue Letter'. This sinister missive used to arrive in a blue envelope and was said to have appeared, out of thin air, in houses across Liverpool in the 1930s, and those who recognised it by its quaint Penny Black stamp, would throw it out of the house immediately, as it was believed to be from the Devil. Those citizens who could not restrain their curiosity and opened the azure envelope, read of something written in blood that was so shocking and terrifying, they died within a week. Even in recent years, the Blue Letter is said

7

to occasionally materialise in houses on Merseyside – you have been warned! Some of the tales included in this volume come straight from a vast, previously unwritten seam of Liverpool folklore, passed down from generation to generation by word of mouth. Where other cultures across the world take pride in preserving their folklore, both oral or written, Liverpool has been careless with her precious legacy and has allowed many of its myths, legends and traditions to vanish into obscurity.

For many years I harboured a dream of having a place in Liverpool which could act as a repository for the city's folklore. I wrote to certain councillors and proposed using the Wellington Rooms on Mount Pleasant – known to most people as the former Irish Centre – as the place where we could store all of the stories I have unearthed about bygone Liverpool. In this Liverpool Folklore & Heritage Centre, there would be volumes about Spring-Heeled Jack, Jenny Greenteeth, Joe Liddle (The Little Storyteller), Tarney, the Scissor Man, and so on. It would be a place where children could visit to learn all about the stories and folklore of our city.

My idea was never taken up, even though the City Council has stated publicly that it was all for promoting Liverpudlian culture. The *Haunted Liverpool* books help to redress this lack of foresight, so that long after this myopic council has passed into obscurity, these tales will still be read and enjoyed, and the fire of imagination will burn bright in the eyes of children who are still unborn.

SEEING THE LIGHT

People talk about 'seeing the light' – a mystical moment in their lives when they suddenly realise the error of their ways, and these revelations can come about in a variety of ways.

A man we shall call John came to see the light in a rather mysterious way in the late 1990s, when he was making a living out of the sale of illegal drugs. John was born in Huyton in the 1970s, and had started out with rather grand plans in life, as almost all children do. At the age of six he decided he wanted to be an astronaut, and developed an interest in stars, comets and planets, and could often be found in his grandmother's garden at night, with his eye glued to a telescope, staring out at the moon and constellations.

John's best friend, who we shall call Alec, wanted to be a musician, and did have a natural talent for playing the classical guitar. They were a very innocent couple of lads, still in the halcyon days of childhood before adolescence reared its ugly head. However, later they both started mixing with the wrong type of people at school, and by the time they were in their late teens, they had both been in trouble with the law. John dropped out of college and was no longer interested in the mystery of the heavens, and Alec sold an expensive acoustic guitar that his mother had bought for his fifteenth birthday. The two youths had lost sight of their dreams, and were soon caught up in the seedy world of petty crime. After a while John and Alec drifted apart and lost touch with one another, and before they knew it, they found themselves in their thirties with a trail of disastrous relationships behind them and very little else. Alec had become a heavy pot smoker who loathed the idea of working for a living, and John survived by selling various illegal drugs. He had developed two obsessions; a fascination with fast cars and looking over his shoulder all the time to check if the police were about.

One day, John was in a city centre pub, talking about his intentions to quit smoking, when a man he had never seen before approached him and said that he had overheard him talking about his decision to stop smoking. The man, who gave his name as Mr Lodge, claimed that he was a qualified clinical hypnotist who had developed a unique hypnotic technique that was guaranteed to make a person stop smoking.

"Hypnotise me now then if you can. Go on, let's see if it works," John challenged the hypnotist.

"I'm afraid not," said Lodge. "The technique will only work in a quiet environment, away from any disturbance. I have an office in Rodney Street but it's currently being redecorated."

"Oh yeah! Sounds like a feeble excuse to me. Knew you couldn't cure me."

"Look, I know I can help you," persisted the stranger. "Would you like me to come to your home? All I need is a quiet space to be able to perform my hypnotherapy."

John was still sceptical and asked to see some kind of business card which would prove that the man was what he claimed he was. Mr Lodge quickly obliged and, taking out his wallet, produced a professional looking embossed card with an ornate border, that read:

Dr Simon Lodge, BSc(Hons), MSc, PhD
Qualified Hypnotist and Regression Therapist
10 Rodney Street
Liverpool
Email: simonlodge@minister.com

John studied the card and put it in his inside pocket, then asked Dr Lodge if he could buy him a drink, but the hypnotist said he had an appointment quite soon and would be leaving the bar shortly. John would have preferred to have got to know the doctor a little better before putting his trust in him, but he was desperate to give up smoking and therefore gave him his home address and made an appointment to see him on the following day.

As agreed, Dr Lodge turned up at John's house at the pre-arranged time. He instructed him to sit on the sofa and make himself as comfortable as possible, and within minutes the hypnotherapy session was underway. The last thing John remembered before slipping into unconsciousness was Dr Lodge saying in a soothing voice, "Think of a place and a time where you were loved."

When John came out of the trance, he was in tears and curled up on the sofa in the foetal position. It was now evening, and the light of a lamppost shone into the deserted room. Dazed and disorientated, he stumbled into the hallway where he found a pile of envelopes on the doormat. He then went into the kitchen where he turned on the light and looked at the clock. It said 8.30pm. There were six recorded messages on his answer-phone, all from underworld contacts asking him where he was. John couldn't understand why he felt so dehydrated, famished and light-headed. When he rang one of his contacts it slowly dawned on him what had happened – he had lost twenty-four hours of his life – or at least he had no recollection of what had happened to him during those hours. He'd been in a trance for an entire day.

There was no sign of Dr Simon Lodge, and John, immediately overcome with the drug dealer's usual paranoia, checked the house from top to bottom in case the hypnotist had stolen money from him, but nothing was amiss. Despite his dry mouth, he picked up a pack of Lambert and Butler and fumbled for a cigarette, his other hand shaking as he thumbed the lighter's wheel. So much for the guaranteed treatment to stop me smoking, John thought. However, the nicotene calmed him somewhat and he sat on the edge of the sofa, and pondered on the strange way he was feeling. It was difficult to define, but he felt as though he'd been through an emotional trauma of some sort. He poured himself a large Smirnoff and gulped it down, then went and retrieved the hypnotherapist's card from his coat pocket and read it again, because he had seriously started to wonder if the man had ever existed at all. It was all so confusing and his head felt so muddled.

On the following evening, as John sat in his BMW at the traffic lights on the Strand, he started to remember everything that he'd experienced whilst under the hypnotic trance. The memories suddenly came flooding back and had soon overwhelmed him. He sat clutching the wheel with tears streaming down his face as he realised what had happened. Then the lights turned to green and he managed to steer the car down Wapping. Through the mysteries of hypnosis, John had somehow been transported back to the age of twelve, and had remained in that state for twenty-four hours, reliving a whole day in his childhood, and it had felt like some divine religious experience. He somehow even knew the exact date of the day that he had relived – Monday, 7 January 1974 – a very special day. He had written that date in his diary when he was a youngster because on that day he had watched excitedly as Comet Kohoutek tracked across the sky after sunset as a tiny smudge of light. John remembered thinking how incredibly fortunate he was, because that interplanetary wanderer would not be seen again for another 75,000 years.

The retrogression by hypnosis left John a changed man. He was able to see the life he was living in a true light and it filled him with revulsion and self-disgust. He relinquished his life of crime and moved back to the neighbourhood of his childhood. The people he'd had criminal dealings with assumed that John had suffered a drug-induced nervous breakdown and never bothered him again. He secured lowly but honest employment as a school caretaker, and found the job very satisfying and he sold the expensive car he'd bought with his ill-gotten gains to provide the deposit for a house in the very street where he had lived so happily as a boy.

He often wondered who the mysterious hypnotist was who had brought about the regression which had enabled him to put his life back on track, and so, out of curiosity, he found himself one day standing outside the address written on the card – Number 10 Rodney Street – and was disappointed to learn from the receptionist that no one by the name of Lodge had ever had an office there. John then remembered the email address on the card and rushed home to his computer, but his email brought no response from the doctor either. Whoever, or whatever, Dr Simon Lodge was, John longed to thank him for his redemption. He hadn't managed to cure his addiction to smoking, but much more importantly, he had enabled John to see the light in a beautiful, yet life-changing, way – by reminding him of the innocent child he had once been –that child who was filled with so many dreams and ambitions.

Here is a question for you to think about. If you could meet the person you were when you were six years old, do you think he or she would be disappointed to see how you have turned out today?

MACKABY'S SCAM

The pub where the idea was hatched was called Gregson's Well, and it stood on the corner of Brunswick Road and Radcliffe Street. The pub had been named after William Gregson, Lord Mayor of Liverpool in 1769, and owner of a important water well on the estate where the drinking establishment now stood.

It was a warm May afternoon in 1954, and sixty-year-old Stanley Mackaby was sitting in a corner of the pub parlour, leisurely sipping a pint of bitter as he perused a copy of the *Daily Sketch*. In the last war, far from doing his bit, he had been the archetypal spiv, trading in nylon stockings and pineapple chunks and doing very nicely thank you, whilst his contemporaries were dying like flies all over the world. In the post-war years he had continued his shady dealings in the black market with moderate success, but nowadays he felt like a dinosaur. Younger, sharper racketeers and confidence tricksters were appearing on the scene every day, and he had lost his footing in this murky underworld.

Becoming obsolete was depressing enough, but Stanley also had another, more pressing, problem that was nagging him day and night; the thousand pounds he owed a local moneylender. Five months previously he had borrowed the money for a shaky business venture that had fallen through, and now he was faced with three alternatives: pay up, endure a severe beating, or flee to Australia. He was puffing heavily on a Woodbine, desperately trying to come up with some way to repay the moneylender, when his old friend Charlie Harris came into the parlour. He sat at Stanley's table and poured a bottle of Mackeson's stout into a half-pint glass as he read the lines in his friend's face. "Die if you worry, die if you don't," he said to Stanley.

"I'm not worrying," protested Stan. "I'm just scheming. I've somehow managed to save a hundred quid by scrimping and saving, but I still need another nine-hundred, or I'm in big, big trouble."

Stanley Mackaby leaned forward, his chin resting on his fist – just like Rodin's sculpture of The Thinker. His expression kept changing; one minute his eyes became animated and he smiled – then the next minute would crease up into deep furrows. He muttered to himself for a while, then suddenly announced:

"I've got it!"

"Go on then," said Charlie Harris, lighting a Senior Service cigarette.

"Now be a good listener for a minute," Stanley told him excitedly. "Imagine if I put a hundred quid on a horse that's eight to one at Sandown. This horse wins ... so I get nine hundred quid back."

"*If* it wins ..." Charlie Harris grinned through his wrinkles.

"That's the point ... it will. Listen, it's all down to Freddie Fisher, the mimic. He can impersonate anyone's voice, you've heard him many a time. Now imagine if we recorded our own version of the race commentary on that reel to reel tape recorder you've got, with Freddie as the commentator. We somehow connect it to the big loudspeaker in the betting shop, and when Brian the bookie hears the results, he assumes he's hearing the official results ... and he pays up... brilliant! If he later realised what'd happened, it'd be too late tough, and he couldn't prove anything anyway."

Charlie grimaced. "Mm ... sounds like a totally crackpot idea to me. It's far too complicated, Stan, and Brian the bookie would never pay that much out, would he?"

"He paid six-hundred nicker out to Ian Washington last year, didn't he?" said Stanley with a mischievous smirk. "I'm going to risk it. I've got nothing to lose and I've got to do something ... and fast."

That afternoon the scam was rehearsed and planned with military precision. Stanley called in at the betting shop for reconnaissance purposes and, trying to look as casual as possible, took careful note of the loose wire leading up to the loudspeaker box. He calculated that he only had to shave a small piece of the insulation off the wire and temporarily connect the two wires from the tape recorder's output socket ... then ... bingo!

That evening Freddie Fisher recorded the bogus commentary, and injecting the same level of excitement into his voice as the usual commentator, and taking his voice off to a tee, reported that a horse called Wistman's Wood had won the 4 o'clock race at Taunton. The recording was very convincing and Stan was beside himself with glee, jumping up and down and hugging Freddie Fisher.

The next day the scam worked perfectly. The betting shop was fairly crowded, and Brian the bookmaker was successfully distracted by Freddie, who started singing a Frankie Laine song at the top of his voice as Stanley hooked the wires up to the existing speaker wires and Charlie cheekily plugged the tape machine (which was housed in a suitcase) into a mains socket. Seconds later the race commentary from the tape was booming out of the shop speaker, ending, of course, with victory for Wistman's Wood at 8-1. Brian the bookie had no choice and he begrudgingly paid out the nine hundred pounds to a jubilant Stanley. The whole betting shop erupted because their had never been such a big win before. all the regular punters crowded round Stan, patting him on the back and shaking his hand, in the hope of a free pint in the pub later.

By a strange coincidence, Wistman's Wood actually did win that day at Taunton at 20-1 odds, which meant that Stan would have won two and a half times as much if he had placed the bet legitimately.

NEMESIS

Early one sunny morning in the late summer of 1967, Stephen Scott, a twenty-year-old mechanic from Halewood, mounted his Vespa 180 Super Sport scooter and rode down a meandering ribbon of road through mist-ghosted expanses of fields chequered with the gold of wheat and the silver of rye. On the Widnes horizon, factory chimneys dumped their incalculable volumes of chemical pollution into the immense blue heavens, and high above the billowing, noxious cumulus cloud, a tranquil morning moon hung in the all-encompassing sky.

Feeling like a truly free spirit on this fresh and beautiful morning, Stephen's thoughts turned, as usual, to his beloved Laura, who was probably still tucked up in her bed over in Runcorn. Upon this Saturday morning, the life he led in Halewood five days a week dwindled into the ever-increasing distance behind him, out of sight and out of mind now, until the following Monday. As he crossed the Silver Jubilee Bridge into Runcorn, the Vespa startled a murmuration of starlings roosting in the steel arches, and they chattered and shrieked as they flew in manic inter-crossing semi-circles back to their spectacular perches.

At just after 9 o'clock he reached Laura's home and waited at the kerbside by her front gate, alternating glances between the grass-green door and her bedroom window. He wouldn't dare knock because her parents didn't approve of him. The door finally opened, but it was Laura's ten-year-old sister Julie who came out on to the doorstep in her nightdress with a piece of toast in her hand. Then Laura appeared behind her and gently tickled the back of the child's head. Julie stepped aside and her seventeen-year-old big sister came to the gate and glanced at Stephen coolly and dispassionately as she put on her pink crash helmet. "Get in, Julie," she said, dismissing her curious younger sister, then opened the gate and stepped into the quiet street. She said nothing as she climbed up on to the pillion seat, but her embrace said it all as she hugged Stephen's waist. The single cylinder, two-stroke engine carried the young couple off into the glorious Saturday morning.

Almost an hour later they stopped off at the Marigold Café near Frodsham and Laura drank a Pepsi through a paper barber-pole straw and he enjoyed a coffee and a cigarette. The place looked like a typical 1940s tea room. Stephen and Laura chatted affectionately in the window seat, and at one point she wanted to hold his hand on the table but for some reason he wouldn't take it, so she started to sulk. He avoided looking at her and lit a cigarette. His face remained turned away from her morose, mascara-rimmed eyes for some time as he studied the street-life through the window.

On the pavement outside, an old woman stood beneath the striped canopy of the café, and she was staring directly at Stephen with an unnerving expression of subdued glee. Her face was withered, wrinkled and pale, and her large, black eyes seemed to bore right through him. She wore a viridian green headscarf, knotted at the saggy underside of her reptilian neck. The repulsive old woman suddenly winked at him, before turning around and became fixated on someone else. Stephen shuddered – there was something about her that made him feel uncomfortable.

On the second floor of a house across the street, a middle-aged man was foolishly edging across his way across the outside ledge of one of the windows, clutching a chamois leather in his hand. Stephen followed the old woman's gaze and suddenly noticed this man, who was obviously taking a very big risk, just just for the sake of clean windows.

What happened next seemed to be played out in slow motion. The man suddenly lost his footing and slipped, desperately trying to grasp the window fame to save himself, but within seconds he had fallen on to the railings below.

Stephen automatically jumped up and ran out of the café. He dashed across the road and as he approached the tragic scene, he was aware of other people converging on the same spot. The man was impaled on the railings, his body bent at an unnatural angle. He was coughing up quantities of vivid red oxygenated blood from his lungs. A man who called the accident victim by his first name held his hand and screamed for some of the bystanders to phone for an ambulance and one of them suddenly snapped out of his spell of morbid fascination and ran to the nearest telephone call box.

Meanwhile, blood blossomed rapidly over the accident victim's white shirt, and Stephen felt nauseous when he suddenly noticed the points of two of the railings protruding from the contours of the man's shoulder blades, which were visible through the blood-soaked shirt.

"Hang on, Harry," implored the man's friend, trying to reassure him. "The ambulance will be here soon. You're going to be alright."

Then the wizened old woman in black elbowed her way to the man's side, and

17

said something which was outrageously insensitive. "Oh, he's done for alright," she intoned in a voice that bordered on a wail. "He won't survive the hour. Look, he's bleeding to death."

The impaled man's friend was so incensed by her words, that he was actually lost for a reply for a few moments, before he let out a string of expletives and profanities that he hadn't used for years, but she was completely oblivious and just kept on repeating her dire predictions.

The skewered man suddenly started to shake violently, and with an indescribable expression on his face, looked directly into his friend's eyes which were now brimming with tears. He then coughed up a great river of blood which splattered his friend's face and clothes, and then he died with blood dripping in a steady stream from his open mouth. Stephen was stunned. He thought about the number of times in the past that people had said that you never know what's around the next corner. Now he knew exactly what they were talking about, but little did he know then, that something even closer to home would reinforce the truth of that saying before the day was out.

The old woman vanished into the crowd.

When Stephen returned to the Marigold Café, still in shock, he told Laura about the terrible accident. She listened quietly and then said that she no longer wanted to go shopping in Chester, which had been their vague plan for that Saturday afternoon. Laura couldn't say why she didn't want to go to Chester, but Stephen sensed what the reason was. It was not because of the accident but because he hadn't wanted to hold her hand at the table. The last time she had reacted in this way was when he refused to say that he loved her when she called him at the garage where he worked in Halewood. He did love her, there was no question of that, but like many men, he found it very hard to show his feelings in public, especially in front of his workmates.

Laura announced that she was going home, and that she preferred to take the bus because she had a headache, and didn't fancy riding pillion passenger on the Vespa. Stephen tried to insist on taking her back to Runcorn, but she was adamant that she would catch the bus home from Frodsham, and she stormed off in a huff without even kissing him goodbye.

A fine day this was turning out to be after such a promising start. Stephen rode off just as a fire engine and ambulance were arriving in the street, sadly too late to save the impaled man. Aimlessly, the young Halewood man drove down highways and country lanes, but found it impossible to escape the haunting face of Laura in his mind's eye. She was definitely the girl he wanted to marry, even though his father had told him to take his time and not to rush into marriage, and in spite of Laura's parents' opposition to him. They felt that he was beneath their daughter for some reason, but he knew without a doubt that he would one day marry her and start a family.

As Stephen was travelling down a narrow road bordered by high hedges on either side in the wilds of Hatchmere, a stolen car came hurtling round the bend at over fifty miles per hour and hit his Vespa head on. What happened after the impact was all so dreamlike and unreal. Stephen spun round and left the ground with twirling fragments of the scooter following him through the air.

Then total blackness.

When he awakened he felt nothing. Lying on his back, gazing up at the sky, which now looked a slightly darker shade of periwinkle blue, he first became aware of the branch of a tree swaying above him. For how long had he lain there? It was impossible to say. The birds were singing and he occasionally heard the faint drone of a bee passing by. He tried to open his mouth to shout for help, but his lips and tongue failed to respond. He tried to blink, but even that was impossible to achieve. Next he felt an urge to inhale deeply, but could barely draw any air into his mouth.

Stephen's mind was working perfectly and he immediately began to wonder if he had broken his neck in the crash. That would explain his paralysis. A green bottle fly landed on his cheek, and crawled up to the rim of his eye. What pure torture that was, as the green bottle drank the lacrimal fluid from the rim of his eyeball. Stephen was powerless to shoo the filthy fly away, and was forced to watch it, out-of-focus, rubbing its legs together as it groomed itself, after taking its fill. It then crawled over to his mouth – which was open. He knew this because he felt the green bottle crawl over his bottom lip and on to his dry tongue. He concentrated his meagre willpower to inhale some air, and the fly, sensing the slight influx of air, flew off.

All sense of time was gone, and the minutes seemed to elongate into hours in his personal limbo. A plane crossed the blue sky as a tiny speck, and Stephen prayed, rather naively, that the people onboard that aircraft would spot him and the remains of his Vespa down below. He mind turned to Laura, and was overcome with unbearable sadness. Then he thought of God. If you are there, please help me, he pleaded, over and over. He had never attended church since he was at school, but now he promised the Creator that he would do so in the future, if he would only send someone to rescue him. He realised that he was in the bottom of a ditch and that passing motorists would be unable to see him. His only hope was a pedestrian, but who would be likely to be walking along this stretch of road?

A century of subjective, personal time passed by, and with it, a hundred mentally voiced cries for help. The sky slowly darkened by degrees, and an ominous chill invaded the only part of Stephen's body in which he still had any sensation – his face.

Then came a sound, barely perceptible at first, but as it slowly filtered through to his brain, he realised that it was a human voice. Someone had come to his rescue and now it was only a matter of time before he would be receiving proper medical attention. That someone was a vagrant, a man with a curly white beard and a blotchy, weather-beaten face and deep-set eyes who loomed into Stephen's restricted field of vision and looked down at him.

"You alive or dead, lad?" he asked.

Stephen mustered all of his will-power, every last ounce of his volition, to move a hand, or twitch a finger, but the impulses failed to reach any of his muscles and he lay there, totally inert.

"Let's see now," said the tramp, kneeling by the side of the young man. "What have we got here?"

After gazing into his apparently lifeless eyes and waving his hand in front of them a few times and getting no response – he began to rummage about in Stephen's jacket, rifling through the pockets. The mechanic was so furious, so utterly disappointed, just when he thought he was about to be saved. His so-called helper had taken his wallet. He caught a glimpse of Laura's photograph in the wallet, and then had to watch as that grimy tramp pulled the precious photograph out, after removing the paper money and the coins – and kissed it – He then took off his coat and wiping the sweat from his brow, bent down out of Stephen's sight. He wondered if he was about to rob his shoes; this man would stoop to anything.

This was surely Hell, trapped in a body which appeared dead to the world. Although he hated the repulsive parasite who had failed him so badly, in some strange way he missed his company as soon as the tramp had wandered away. Night eventually descended, and all Stephen could see were a few stars peppering the black sky and the silhouette of the overhanging tree branch swaying in the breeze. Occasionally, the sound of a car could be heard in the lane, and each time Stephen fervently prayed for them to stop, but they all passed by, and he was left in the ditch, hidden by the tall grass.

Later that night, it was impossible to say when, something dark came down out of the starry sky. It looked like a fluttering black sheet, but there was a white smudge in the middle of it. Stephen could see that it was going to land on him, and he mentally braced himself for the impact. As the thing drew closer, his heart sank as he realised that the white patch in the middle of it was the face of that repellant old woman he had seen outside the café; the one who had probably terrified the man on the railings into an even swifter death. She grinned at the paralysed mechanic from the middle of the black flapping cloth and her face crawled about like a thousand worms and her eyes widened to saucers as she came nearer.

"I am your Nemesis," she cried, in a raspy, unearthly voice.

"Nooo!" Stephen managed to scream out at last, at which the old hag instantly vanished. Thank goodness, his speech had returned at last …

… But it all proved to be a cruel dream; he'd merely drifted off to sleep and experienced a nightmare. The stars were still above him, only they had moved a few degrees towards the west and Stephen eventually became resigned to his fate. He would die here all alone, far from his family, and far away from his beloved Laura. How he wished he could hold hands with her now as she had wanted him to in the café. He felt totally bereft, as if God had been nothing but a false hope, a mere fairy tale character who he had turned to in this extreme predicament. He drifted off to sleep again, and this time he was thinking only of Laura. But then he experienced another very strange dream. A radiant man in a white gown came down from the sky and lifted Stephen from the ditch and placed him near the roadside. The figure was softly spoken and had reassured him that help would come arrive.

He awakened with a start – and immediately noticed that the tree branch above him was missing. It hadn't been a dream at all; he had been moved. The sky was blue once more, and a skylark was flying overhead, calling for its mate. Stephen's face still felt slightly numb. As time dragged by, he started to feel a slight sensation in his stomach. He recognised that sensation, it was hunger. A butterfly landed on his face, and he desperately wanted it to stay there. It represented life and was the only company he had, but soon it fluttered away … because something had startled it. Voices could be heard nearby. "Come on! Find me please!" Stephen cried out in his mind.

And they did find him. Two policemen appeared in front of him and one knelt by his side and looked into his eyes.

"Looks like a goner," he sighed, shaking his head. "Only young as well."

"Yeah, what a waste," said the other policeman, who was out of Stephen's field of vision. "Wonder where he got that old coat from?" he added, looking at the old trench coat draped over him. The tramp had put it there of course, perhaps out of sympathy for the young man, or maybe guilt, or perhaps because it was full of holes and too heavy to wear on a hot day. Whatever the reason, that coat had prevented Stephen from dying of hypothermia during the night.

"Hey! His eyelid just moved. Look!" one of the policemen cried, drawing his colleague's attention to a slight twitch in his eye.

"You're right, call for an ambulance."

"You're going to be alright, lad. We'll take you to the hospital right now and they'll soon fix you up," said the policeman, who remained at Stephen's side.

Stephen was taken to Chester Royal Infirmary, where, due to the skills of dedicated hospital surgeons and nurses, he made a gradual recovery. It transpired that the man who had stolen the car that had smashed into Stephen had been caught later that day and he'd confessed to the police about the collision on the bend in the road. The police had found the wreckage of the Vespa scooter, but had been unable to find Stephen in that ditch and assumed that he had been able to walk away from the crash. Stephen told the doctor and one of the policemen who had found him that he had been near a tree, and how all he had been able to see was a piece of the sky and an overhanging branch. The policeman looked puzzled and said that they had found him nowhere near a tree. He was on the roadside.

Who then, had moved him? Had the dream about being moved by the kind glowing figure in the white garment been an actual memory of some intervention by an angel? Was the dream of the old woman in black been nothing more than a nightmare, or had she too been real? She had definitely been a real person at the scene of horrific accident facing the café. Stephen asked the doctor what 'Nemesis' meant, because the evil-looking woman had said, "I am your Nemesis."

The doctor said he didn't know, and suggested that the angel and the Nemesis woman had been merely dreams and hallucinations caused by Stephen's injuries, and he advised him to rest. Laura, however, was curious about the meaning of Nemesis and she went to her local library and did some research.

She shuddered when she discovered that it was the ancient name of a fabled remorseless goddess of death and vengeance.

Stephen and Laura gradually put the mysterious events surrounding his accident behind them and when he was fully recovered, he took Laura to the Marigold Café in Cheshire and lovingly held her hands across the table, for everyone to see. After telling her how much he loved her, he produced an engagement ring, and got down on his knees. All of the mellowed old customers smiled at the heart-warming sight, and when Laura answered, "Yes, I will", they rushed over to congratulate the couple.

SARAH AND THE WIZARD

One grey Saturday afternoon on a rain-soaked street off Liverpool's Brownlow Hill, long ago in Victorian times, a riot of poor but clean children were laughing and playing. They sang ancient rhymes, which had been passed down from one generation of children to the next, as the beautiful Fairhurst sisters stood at each end of a rope, turning it with controlled hypnotic grace as the skipping boys and girls chanted:

> *On the Mount there is a Lady,*
> *Who she is I do not know,*
> *All she wants is gold and silver,*
> *All she wants is a very fine beau...*

Little six-year-old Lucy Magowan skipped in time with the flat-capped boys and the half-starved barefoot girls as the skipping rope swept above and below them, and her sky-blue Celtic eyes were aglow as she took her turn to sing the next line of the song: "Calling in my very best friend, very best friend, very best friend..." she sang, and she had the voice of a cherub. Her thin, tall, seven-year-old companion, Maggie Jones – also known as 'Skinny M'link' – giggled as she took up Lucy's invitation and joined in the skipping game. She dashed from the kerb and started jumping up and down with the rest of the gang as the skipping rope rhythmically turned.

The year was 1879 and the month was March and those seven children skipping and singing were oblivious to a poor, twelve-year-old Sarah Williams, who was making her escape at that very moment from the miseries of the Liverpool Workhouse across the road. How the escape was accomplished was never determined with any factual certainty, as Sarah was a fantasy-prone child with an epic imagination, who spun tales as long and colourful as those of Homer, and she related numerous, conflicting versions of her dramatic breakout. Whatever the details, the escape was somehow achieved, and after she had sprung from the workhouse that Spring, the little urchin laid low for a while somewhere amongst the dark alleyways in the great city. However, the resourceful child was determined that those dank alleyways would not be her home for long and she already knew exactly where she was going.

When twilight descended, she paid a visit to the grand home of Mrs Caledonia Rogers on Bedford Street South, an address she knew because up to a few years ago Sarah's mother had been a lady's maid at the American woman's residence. The widowed Elizabeth Williams had left her employment after falling for the charms of an Australian man, Billy Wain. For a time she thought she could look forward to a lifetime of married bliss, but she was soon disillusioned when it was later discovered that Billy had a wife and three children back in Perth. The shocking truth came to light on the very day before Elizabeth was due to marry Billy, and the shock so weakened her that she died from a fever a month later. Young Sarah, who had diligently acted as sick-nurse to her mother, understood very well that she had died from a broken heart.

As an orphan, with no means of support, Sarah was duly placed in the Liverpool Workhouse. Now, after her daring escape from the soul-destroying drudgery within those walls, Sarah arrived at Number 83 Bedford Street late at night under the cover of darkness and rang the bell. When he opened the door, the old butler, Chattersby, barely recognised the child. She was older and taller than the little Sarah he had known. Not until the unkempt, dirty-faced child in workhouse clothes spoke did Chattersby realise who she was. Within minutes, Sarah Williams was being embraced by Caledonia Rogers in the drawing room. The fifty-five-year-old ex-belle of New Orleans cried with the child after hearing her tragic story. Without any hesitation, she decided to adopt the girl as if she were her own.

Sarah Williams was soon enjoying a life that was different in every possible way from her previous existence. She was dressed in the most expensive fashions of the day, and rode about in a carriage with Mrs Rogers, who informed any inquisitive acquaintances that the girl was her niece. A detective named Connor, investigating Sarah's escape from the workhouse, paid Caledonia Rogers a visit, but the butler refused to allow him over the threshold, saying that the lady of the house was unwell. This wasn't purely an evasion tactic; a virulent fever was rampant in Liverpool at the time, and Mrs Rogers was feeling off colour and had lost her appetite. Connor promised that he'd return in a few days' time. He also claimed that Sarah Williams had stabbed the master of the workhouse in the arm during her escape, and so the child would be brought before a court of law when she was found. Sarah became distressed when Mrs Rogers confronted her with the policeman's accusation and asked if it was true. Looking her straight in the eye, she explained that she had merely scratched him because he had been swinging her around his office by her hair, and it hurt.

Worried that Sarah's version of events might not be believed, even though she was certain it was the truth, Caledonia Rogers bundled her off to a private house in North Wales which belonged to a Welsh friend, Mrs Meredith. The front windows of the grand, white-painted house gave on to magnificent views of the Great Orme's Head at Llandudno, and the attic skylight on the other side of the roof afforded breathtaking vistas of distant Snowdonia. Sarah Williams felt as if she had entered a magical world in this bucolic setting, and old Mrs Meredith, who initially greeted the Liverpool girl with a rather stony face, came to know the child and treasure her vivid imagination.

As well as the beautiful scenery, the likes of which Sarah had never seen before, the unfolding summer had plenty of supernatural surprises in store for the girl from Liverpool, and they all started with the sighting of a strange cloud, high above the waters of the Irish Sea one evening at sunset. As the sun dipped into the sea, its blood-orange rays shone into Sarah's bedroom as the girl sat at her open window, dreamily gazing into the malachite-coloured sky at the ever-changing cumulus clouds – when she spotted a cubic one. She couldn't believe her eyes at first, but as the strange cubic-shaped cloud drifted over the house, she could see that its misty interior concealed an actual castle in the air, complete with turrets, towers and battlements. The magical cloud halted directly above the house – and started to descend!

Looking skywards from her window, Sarah was both afraid and amazed by the castle in the air. She ducked back under the window and turned towards the bedroom door, then shouted Mrs Meredith at the top of her voice. The door flew open, and Mrs Meredith came barging in with her forefinger to her lips. "Do be quiet, girl," she whispered, as the house began to sway as if a giant had uprooted it. Soon, clouds of soot started falling down the chimney and a thick black cloud billowed from the fireplace.

By the diffused light of the dying sun, Sarah and the old woman saw the six-foot-tall silhouette of a man with a pointed hat suddenly appear in the gathering amber gloom of the bedroom. He grabbed Sarah by the wrist and she felt all the energy drain out of her body. Mrs Meredith screamed, "No, you cannot take her. She's but a child!" But a second later, Sarah found herself standing on the glittering granite battlements of the castle she had seen in the clouds. The wind was whistling all around her, and she turned to see the man in the black robe with the pointed hat.

"Who are you?" she asked, still feeling weak.

"I am Manannan Mac Lyr – a wizard," said the stranger, "and I have chosen you to be my wife."

His long hair was as black as night and his dark-green eyes twinkled with mischief. He seemed to be about thirty years of age – an old man to Sarah.

She felt dizzy and unsteady on her feet as she looked over the battlements at the limestone rocks of the Great Orme thousands of feet below, tinged with pink from the dying sun. Then she noticed several stone, gargoyle-like creatures, standing like winged sentries along the walls, but they weren't statues at all – because as she watched them they began to move.

The Wizard took the child by the arm and led her through the winding passages of the strange castle until he came to an enormous circular hall with an ancient round wooden table at its centre. Manannan bragged that he had stolen the table from King Arthur long ago, and he sat at the largest chair at this table, then told the Liverpool waif the reason why he had kidnapped her:

"You are the living replica of my first love, my Queen Fand. She left me a long time ago to live with the Fay."

Sarah looked at the wizard blankly; it was all too much to take in.

Manannan smiled and said, "The Fay are what you and your stupid people call the faeries. They live in the Otherworld. Oh, never mind! Sarah, I have been watching you from up here, and I have fallen in love with you. When I ripen you, you shall be my bride."

"Ripen me?" gasped Sarah, horrified at the strange expression, and desperately hoping that this whole thing was a nightmare. "What do you mean?"

Manannan smiled, and explained."I shall age you so that you will become a woman within the span of a minute."

He showed his palms to the frightened girl, and she felt a strange sensation course through her veins. Her body started to expand. Bones and muscles wrenched and cracked and stretched, and her hair began to extend steadily out of her scalp causing a horrible tingling sensation. Sarah complained that her legs were hurting and Manannan cackled. "Growing pains!" he said and his laughter at his own joke echoed around the hall. Within the minute, as he had predicted, Sarah was transformed into a woman ... or at least her body had. Her mind was still that of an innocent, twelve-year-old girl. Through his magic, Manannan then clothed her in a beautiful satin gown, before he embraced and kissed her. All the while he had tears in his eyes.

"Now we shall be married," the wizard whispered in her ear.

27

Manannan's levitating castle circled the world on a grand tour through the skies of the earth, and high up on the castle keep, the magician and his young conquest stood flanked by the gargoylesque guards as they beheld the wonders below; the icy face of Mount Everest, the snaking Great Wall of China, the foaming waters of the Niagara Falls, the Pyramids, the Zulu warriors of the Veldt, the ghostly continent of Antarctica and the ancient grey whales of the Pacific Ocean; all of these amazing sights and spectacles drifted by far below.

During the castle's circumnavigation of the globe it passed over England. Manannan pointed his ringed finger to the cornfields scrolling past a thousand feet below, and using his magic he drew strange circles in the corn, including his own mysterious emblem – the three-legged Triskelion disk. From this great altitude, the baffled farmers and farmhands who were gathering round the crop circles looked like curious ants to Sarah, who was still consumed with sadness at having her childhood snatched away by Manannan. She pined for Simon, the thirteen-year-old Welsh boy she had fallen in love with back in Llandudno. For a moment she recalled his beautiful but unusual eyes; one was blue and the other was green …

"Who is that you're thinking about?" shrieked Manannan, suddenly angry and seizing the girl's face with his pale hand and tightly gripping her jaw. He gazed deep into Sarah's eyes and demanded to know the name of the boy she was thinking of with such sentiment. "Who is he? Tell me!"

"I'm not telling you! I hate you!" Sarah screamed, and leaned on the battlement, sobbing with her face in her hands.

Manannan said something in his native Manx tongue and stormed off into the castle. The citadel descended on to the giant hill of Cronk Sumark and became invisible to all outside of its impenetrable walls. Manannan took Sarah to the coast, where Enbarr, the magician's old seahorse, reared its head from the waters. The creature was armoured like a crab and studded with coloured sea anemones and limpets. Manannan lifted Sarah on to the maritime steed's back and then mounted it himself. Enbarr swam off at great speed into the waters of the Irish Sea and roved for many miles, until twilight fell.

Manannan pleaded with Sarah to love him as they sat on the seahorse being rocked by the waves, with a ship bound for Liverpool drifting past them in the distance. Two sailors onboard the creaking sailing ship were singing a sentimental ballad, and the luminous crimson, green and blue curtains of the Northern Lights wavered in the night sky. It was a perfect moment in time for two lovers to kiss, but Sarah turned a cold cheek to Manannan's caresses. He let out a tremendous cry of pain which echoed like thunder, and flew skywards into the starry heavens, leaving Sarah clinging in terror to Enbarr's mane. Sizzling bolts of green light flew from his fingers and hit the sailing ship, setting her stern alight. Manannan, full of spite because of his unrequited love, then went to torment the Manx keepers of the Chicken Rock Lighthouse with his occult powers. The three keepers gazed in terror beyond the windows of the light-room at the sinister silhouette of the flying figure circling the lighthouse. Manannan conjured up a vast deep whirlpool from which low moaning voices wailed, inspiring fear in the hearts of the lighthouse keepers. Meanwhile, the seahorse took Sarah ashore, and the girl tried to run off, but found her way barred by the twelve-foot-high figure of one of the winged gargoyles whose burning red eyes brought her to an abrupt halt. Manannan returned to the island and dragged a struggling Sarah back to the castle, where she told him she would rather die than become his wife.

But she was powerless to stop him.

The wedding of the wizard Manannan and his child bride Sarah took place in a hollow of white hazel on the Isle of Anglesey, attended by a host of supernatural guests from Magonia, a mystical world in the sky, invisible to ordinary mortals. By this time, the Manx sorcerer had cast a hex on Sarah to make her act as if she loved and adored him, and so, she stood meekly beside him at an ancient megalithic altar in a trance-like state with a constant mindless smile on her face and empty eyes.

To the right of Manannan, clothed in long flowing indigo robes, stood his old flame Jenna Green, a silver-eyed witch of supreme powers who had once been the leader of a coven on the banks of the Mersey many centuries before. Her love for Manannan had conflicted with the interests of the coven and had sparked a war between the witches of Lancashire and the warlocks of Avalon – the former name of the Isle of Man. After the conflict, the Council of Wiccans had exiled Jenna to the Nordic island of Ultima Thule until – after three hundred years of heartache – her love for Manannan had finally died. Today Jenna Green was only remembered in an old Lancashire skipping rope rhyme as, 'Ginny Greenteeth'.

Az, the chief gargoyle sentry of Manannan, brought a highly revered artefact to the altar, and everyone bowed upon seeing it. It was known as the Vessel of Plenty and the Holy Grail amongst other names, and it shone with a spiritual light. Lies could not be uttered in its presence, and it could magically provide strange, manna-like food which gave immense courage to those who ate it. The vessel was created during a golden age of mankind, long before the worldwide floods and catastrophes had plunged civilisation into the dark ages. The most sacred feature of the Grail was the Truth Talker. When questions were pitched at the cup, a small glowing cherubic head rose from it, and invariably gave a truthful answer. The Truth Talker officiated at this wedding, and duly rose up from the cup. The small mouth fluttered and asked Manannan if he loved Sarah with all of his heart.

"I do," he replied.

The iridescent head then asked Sarah if she loved the wizard with all of her heart, and she couldn't utter a word of reply, because only Manannan's spell made her act as if she loved him, and the Truth Talker sensed this. The sparkling head thus announced: "This wedding shall not be, for it is not truthful!"

With a whistling sound, the head vanished back into the cup, and Manannan lunged at it with rage, but Jenna Green and three other wizards held him back, knowing he'd be struck dead if he tried to harm the Grail. Az returned the sacred relic to a secret place on the island, and Manannan and Jenna returned to the castle in the air with Sarah. Manannan was so distraught, he began to lose faith in himself. "Why will you not love me?" he screamed at Sarah, who fell down crying. Manannan could stop the world turning, but he couldn't make the Liverpool waif love him. Suddenly, Sarah began to writhe on the floor. Her body was returning to normal – to that of a child again, and the wizard looked on in horror as her womanly form was lost amongst the swathes of her ivory and silver wedding gown. Her rejection of his love was so powerful that it had overcome his powers. Manannan felt weakened. The castle was falling …

Manannan's castle plummeted like a millstone through the dense clouds, but the ruby-eyed gargoyle sentries remained loyally at their posts, seconds away from doom, as Manannan lay prostrate on the floor, robbed of his powers by a crisis of intense self-doubt. And all because Sarah had resisted his will and refused to love him. Now her childhood had been restored by the forces of nature and she stood trembling before him, swamped by the elaborate, full-sizes wedding dress.

A long time ago, in the days before William the Conqueror arrived in England, the English alphabet had seven more letters, and these letters, in the right combination, had powerful magical properties, but they became abused by base sorcerers and necromancers, so Merlin had removed them from the alphabet. The lost letters of the English alphabet were still known to Jenna Green, and she used them to recite strange-sounding words as she cast a hex. Once the words of spoken magic were uttered, Sarah suddenly found herself on the northern shore of Anglesey. Jenna appeared next to her, embracing a semi-conscious Manannan. The child followed Jenna's gaze and looked out to sea – just in time to catch a glimpse of the falling castle, a mile or so in the distance. As the citadel hit the waters it exploded into thousands of fragments, throwing jets of spray and steam hundreds of feet into the air. Thunder from the blast rolled across the island, and Manannan gazed tearfully towards the horizon and whispered, "Az," the name of his chief gargoyle. Jenna then gently asked Sarah if she would like to go home, and the girl nodded.

"Then think of home and you shall be there," the witch told her, but before she did so, Manannan suddenly took off a small silver ring from his little finger and gave it to Sarah.

"Remember me please, Sarah," he said, his voice breaking. Moments later, Sarah Williams found herself dressed in her old familiar clothes back in the Liverpool home of Caledonia Rogers at Number 83 Bedford Street. She ran into the parlour and startled the fifty-five-year-old American woman, who looked pale and quite ill.

"Oh, Sarah, what are you doing here?" asked Caledonia.

Sarah rattled off her incredible story of the wizard, but she wasn't believed, of course. That night, Caledonia slipped into a coma, and a physician opined that the former southern belle had a blood-clot on the brain and that she was unlikely to see morning. Sarah crept to the dying woman's bedside that night, and with tears flooding down her cheeks, the girl begged Caledonia to get better. As she lifted her head, she suddenly heard Manannan's voice as a faint echoing whisper.

"Place the silver ring under her tongue."

Sarah took Manannan's ring off her finger, gently opened Caledonia's mouth, and placed it under her tongue as directed by the ghostly voice. Her benefactress began to stir. She smiled. Her large blue eyes opened – brimming with life. She sat up in the bed immediately, and with a quizzical expression, she reached into her mouth and removed the ring. Sarah hugged the widow and Caledonia embraced the child back. Mrs Rogers made a full recovery, and each day she would ask Sarah to go over the strange tale of the wizard from the Isle of Man. The child was a natural storyteller, but how on earth would she have been able

31

to make up such an unusual story? Furthermore, Mrs Meredith arrived at the house shortly afterwards, confirming the account of Sarah's abduction, and stranger still, the old Welsh woman said that she had heard all about the wizard Manannan from her grandmother, who had also been kidnapped by him many years ago.

Sadly, in the following year, Caledonia Rogers fell ill once again, and this time, Sarah cried bitterly, because she had lost the silver ring, and she was unable to prevent the American widow from passing away.

Sarah later married her childhood sweetheart Simon in Wales, and they produced many children.

I hope Manannan rekindled his love for Jenna Green, the witch who once had a coven on the Mount next to St James's Cemetery. She is now long forgotten, and is only remembered in that skipping rope rhyme:

On the Mount there is a Lady,
Who she is I do not know,
All she wants is gold and silver,
All she wants is a very fine beau ...

THE LILY WHITE BOYS

Hardly a year goes by without a sighting of the mysterious 'Lily White Boys' – let me explain. The Earth has twelve moons for each month of the calendar year: the Wolf Moon, the Snow Moon, the Worm Moon, the Pink Moon, the Flower Moon, the Strawberry Moon, the Buck Moon, the Sturgeon Moon, the Harvest Moon, the Hunter's Moon, the Beaver Moon, and the Cold Moon. Of course, there is only one actual moon, but different cultures in different time periods have perceived and celebrated our natural satellite in a multitude of ways.

The Harvest Moon is no ordinary full moon because it behaves in a rather special manner. Throughout our year the moon rises about fifty minutes later each night. However, near the autumnal equinox, the day-to-day difference in the local time of moonrise is only half an hour. Harvest Moon is determined as the full moon that falls nearest to the autumnal equinox, around 23 September, but sometimes the nearest full moon will fall in October. In 2006, the Harvest Moon rose on Saturday 7 October. The Harvest Moon became the traditional date when pagans would thank Mother Nature for a successful harvest. When Christianity spread to Britain, the cult of the Harvest Moon was observed on the Sunday closest to that full moon, and thus began the ritual of the Harvest Festival, a noble custom in which adults and children bring food to schools and churches as a reminder of all the good things God gives to the human race. This food is parcelled up and given away to the needy.

The Harvest Moon is apparently also one of the dates marked by a mysterious cult that is said to predate Christianity – that of the Lily White Boys. One of the earliest mentions of this obscure cult, which practises animal and allegedly child sacrifice, is in an ancient folk song entitled, 'Green Grow the Rushes O'. A line of that song states, 'Two, two, lily-white boys, clothed all in green'. Such green-robed figures have been seen for hundreds of years across the land, including the North West of England. They congregate around this time of the year at four locations: Wirral's Bidston Hill, a field between Waddicar and Melling, Bowring Park, and the Delamere Forest.

One Harvest Moon night in the 1970s, Brian and Tina, a young couple travelling homewards down Bull Bridge Lane in Aintree, came across a circle of figures in green robes standing in a field around a bonfire, and one of the figures was holding what looked like a small, doll-like effigy. Brian got out of his car near the River Alt to get a better look at the strange ceremony, and asked an old passer-by what was going on.

"I'm afraid it's the Lily White Boys burning a child," said the oldster, gravely, "and if you've got any sense, you won't go anywhere near them, or they're just as likely to kill you as well."

"You're joking," said Brian. "That's just some Guy Fawkes thing they're burning – isn't it?"

But the old man shook his head solemnly.

Brian raced home and called the police, but the only thing that remained in the smouldering vestiges of the bonfire by the time the police arrived were the charred remains of a sheep.

Further back in time, in 1941, some World War Two ARP wardens were livid when they spotted the flames of a huge bonfire lighting up fields for miles around at Bowring Park. The wardens set off to investigate and were stopped in their tracks when they came upon a group of green-robed men and naked women dancing around the fire, and five of these men, wielding vicious-looking scythes and swords, chased the wardens away. They returned with a few policemen, and were given the fairly innocent explanation that the Lily White Boys had simply been conducting a thanksgiving ritual, and had burned several sheep in the course of the ceremony.

On another occasion during the war, this time on Walpurgis night – 30 April – the green-clad figures were gathered around a fire close to what is now Childwall Golf Course, when the ARP wardens and police confronted them – only to watch as the fire and the figures – spookily fade away before their eyes. The locals said this was a ghostly re-enactment of a medieval gathering of the Lily White Boys.

Many years ago, a certain prominent politician passed away, and his wife discovered, among his belongings, a mysterious green robe and matching pointed hood, similar to those worn by the Ku Klux Klan. She assumed it was some kind of Masonic regalia, but she later received a sinister threatening letter, warning her to burn the robe, and the epistle was signed LWB, an abbreviation for the Lily White Boys.

If you should see any bonfires on your travels around Walpurgis Night, or at the time of the Harvest Moon – keep well away from them!

THE LOCKET

In the autumn of 1977, a series of eerie incidents took place at a house on Gelling Street in Toxteth, which defy a rational explanation to this day. It all began on the Tuesday night of 27 September 1977, when John Warren had just finished painting the master bedroom of the house. His wife Maureen cooked John a fish and chip supper, and then they both retired to their son Malcolm's bedroom to sleep in his single bed, because the noxious fumes from the paint were overpowering in the master bedroom. Malcolm was staying at his grandmother's in Everton for the night, and Mr and Mrs Warren were the only people at home.

The couple laughed as they tried to settle down and get comfortable in the single bed, and it brought back memories of the bed they had slept in when they moved into their first flat in Old Swan fifteen years back. A full moon was beaming through the window into the room, and John put his arm around Maureen and kissed her goodnight – then started to doze off. Maureen was trying to get some shut eye too, when the distinctive sweet scent of violets permeated the room. It wasn't related to the sharp aroma from the painted walls of the master bedroom, because the door of the bedroom was tightly shut. The gabble, hubbub and background noises of the day had died down in the street below, and silence hung in the air. Maureen soon drifted off again, but woke some time later to see that the full moon beyond the window had climbed higher in the sky. The sound of voices had awakened her, and they seemed very close – in the room almost. Maureen was now fully awake and heard a man shouting.

"You'd say anything but your prayers, Gertie! I saw you kissing."

A well-spoken woman replied, "Harry, it was a mistake! I love only you! Harry!"

Then a female scream echoed round the moonlit bedroom and quickly faded away. Maureen shook John awake to tell him about the disturbing voices, but her husband's groggy reply was: "You've had a nightmare, Mo. Go back to sleep," and soon he was snoring again. Three more times that night the fragrance of violets returned and permeated the room and thrice the ghostly voices began to argue. On the third instance Maureen heard a heavy thud after the woman's scream. She peeped out from under the blankets and looked at the carpet – and there a woman in old fashioned clothes lay on her back She was aged about thirty-five and her pale ashen face was bathed in the moon's silver rays. Her wide eyes faced up to the ceiling but they looked lifeless. A man could be heard somewhere close by, sobbing loudly, and this time, Maureen's husband was awakened by the lamentations. Finally, here was proof that the strange goings-on were not all in Maureen's mind.

On the following morning, Maureen was making the bed in her son's room when she found an old Victorian, or Edwardian locket under the pillow. Inside the locket there was a miniature, sepia-toned portrait of the very woman she had seen lying prostrate on the floor the night before. When her son returned home she grilled him, demanding to know where he had acquired the locket, and when he eventually admitted the truth, Maureen was shocked to the marrow.

Apparently, Malcolm's friend had ransacked a crumbling tomb in nearby St James's Cemetery, and had removed the locket and other items of jewellery from the exposed corpse. Malcolm had then bought the locket from his friend, intending to give it to his girlfriend as a love token, and he had hidden it under his pillow for safekeeping. Malcolm and his friend had tried to read the engravings on the fallen tombstone, which was heavily encrusted with soil and lichen; the first half of the inscription had been 'Gertrude' but the surname was indecipherable. Maureen shuddered when she heard the name and told her son to get rid of the locket immediately, she didn't want it in the house.

Had Gertrude been murdered in that Gelling Street house and had Maureen somehow witnessed the grisly re-enactment of the crime in her son's bedroom that night? Unfortunately that is not known, but after delving into this case I did find that in 1877 a Gertrude Leavey died, aged thirty-four, in the very house where Maureen Warren lived.

THE UNSEEN

Having spent many years looking into ghosts and other aspects of the paranormal, it has long been clear to me that some people are very receptive to psychic phenomena, whilst others are practically blind to the existence of phantoms and the psychic world.

Why is this so? What makes a person psychic? Do they have to belong to a certain blood group? Is it something in their diet? All of these factors and many others have been taken into account in an effort to build up a 'typical' picture of the psychic personality, but without any success. I have heard people say that vegetarians are more likely to be psychic, yet there are many meat-eating peoples of the world who are legendary mediums, such as the Eskimos, who are traditionally more or less exclusively carnivorous. I have heard certain 'psychic instructors' advising people to take up Buddhism, or to live in isolation in the country and meditate daily in order to develop their psychic skills, but yet I have been dazzled by the mediumship of a mother-of-five children living on a busy council estate in Liverpool.

Seemingly then, no one really knows why certain people are psychic, any more than we can know why other individuals can become great artists or songwriters. It really does seem to be a God-given talent. You could spend hundreds of thousands of pounds – millions even – on a musical student's education and still fail to produce another John Lennon, or Paul McCartney – both of whom could neither write nor read music when they created their most famous songs.

In my time I have heard most of the theories which attempt to explain what makes a person psychic. Gypsies, Celts and Basques are said to have a 'psychic streak' in their blood, which, by the way, is predominantly Rhesus negative, but I don't see what blood has to do with the mysterious talents of clairvoyancy, telepathy, precognition etc. Nor do I see the relevance of a person's bodily shape in relation to their psychic abilities, but the American psychologist William H Sheldon (1898-1977) paved the way for such thinking when he classified the human species into three basic types, which he called the Endomorph, the Mesomorph and the Ectomorph. A number of French researchers took the theories of Sheldon a stage further into the realms of nonsense and claimed that certain people of a particular shape made better psychics than other types.

Then we come to another trendy concept in the paranormal world that was once used to explain everything from UFO sightings to premonitions: Temporal Lobe Epilepsy. This harks back to the 1960s when an anthropologist by the name of Adrian Boshier went to live among primitive tribes in South Africa. Boshier suffered from epilepsy, and the people of the tribe regarded such a neurological disease as something sacred. Soon after they had witnessed him having a fit the anthropologist was made a junior witch doctor. Whilst it may be true that some of the great saints and mystics were said to have been epileptics, it is also true that a far greater number of psychics and clairvoyants have shown no signs of suffering from any such condition.

The following story illustrates the way in which two people – one of them psychic – perceived the same reality in very different ways.

In 1966, a twenty-two-storey tower block called St George's Heights was built on Netherfield Road in Everton. Like many of the tower blocks of the sixties, it was to be rather short-lived and was demolished several years ago. The views from the upper storeys were truly breathtaking on all sides of St George's Heights, with spectacular vistas of the Mersey and the Wirral peninsula to the west, and the panoramic horizons of the semi-rural suburbs chequered in shades of green to the east.

In 1970, two close friends in their early twenties, Carol and Claire, moved into a maisonette flat in Everton, and the view from their new home was dominated by the imposing presence of St George's Heights, which stood just a few hundred yards away. One Friday night the girls were trying on different clothes in preparation for a night out at the Wooky Hollow nightclub. Finally, Carol settled on a Maxi skirt and a sequinned velvet bodice, and Claire donned a pair of hot pants and then squeezed into a risqué bandeau top.

The radio was playing a catchy Clodagh Rogers pop song called 'Goodnight Midnight' and Carol was miming to the song as she gazed intently into the dressing table mirror, applying mascara – when she noticed a creepy but familiar sight. Among the gallery of illuminated yellow squares in the silhouette of St George's Heights, there was one particular window on the eleventh floor with the figure of a man framed within it. This solitary figure was always at that window whenever the girls had their curtains open in the evening, and Carol, who had almost perfect eyesight, had often claimed that the man seemed to be looking through a pair of binoculars, although it was impossible to be certain without using binoculars themselves.

"There's the peeping Tom again," Carol said through gritted teeth, gazing past her reflection in the window towards the myriad lit windows of the tower block.

"Which window tonight?" asked Claire gazing up at the block and Carol pointed. "Don't point, he'll know!" said Claire, and she went to the light switch and plunged the room into darkness.

"There, next to that window with the red curtains," said Carol, pointing at the monolithic building. "See him now?"

"Yes. But how do you know he's looking at us, though? He's looks just like a black spot to me."

Claire squinted at the distant silhouetted figure.

"I've got better eyesight than you, that's why," replied Carol. "I'm certain he's watching us, and he's looking through something like binoculars. Probably a dirty old man."

"Ah well, we should let him have a real eyeful one night and do a strip-tease for him."

The girls found the whole thing rather amusing and carried on with their lengthy and meticulous preparations. Eventually, they were ready for their night out and set off for the club.

A few days later the girls were watching television one evening, when Carol once again drew her flatmate's attention to the watcher in St George's Heights. Shortly afterwards, Claire had to pop round to her mother's home in Tuebrook to borrow some money, and during the visit, she sneaked into her father's room and borrowed his old pair of binoculars, which he used for bird-watching. Upon her return to the flat, she saw that the suspected voyeur was still at his window, and turning off the lights, she trained the binoculars on him. She thumbed the wheel on the field glasses and the mysterious onlooker suddenly swam starkly into focus. He was dark-haired and podgy faced, although it was hard to tell what age he was. He was not looking through binoculars after all, but was staring into the eyepiece of a large telescope of some sort. He shook his head and moved away from the eyepiece, perhaps because he could see nothing now that the girls were in a darkened room.

"Let me see, come on!" said Carol, impatiently urging her friend to pass the binoculars.

"Here, take a look at the thing he's been watching us with," Claire said, handing her the binoculars.

As Carol took her turn to have a look at the peeping Tom, Claire switched the light back on.

Startled, Carol turned around and scowled.

"Turn it off!" she shrieked.

"No, let him see we're watching him. See what he does," replied Claire, heading towards the window with a supercilious grin on her face.

Carol took another look through the binoculars. She was so angry at Claire for switching on the light, that her hands shook, but when she'd steadied herself by resting the binoculars against the window frame, she could clearly saw that the man was back at his telescope. He recoiled away from the eyepiece when he saw that he was now the one being watched now. He turned to face Carol, and she could just make out his worried expression. He darted away from the window and then the light went out in his room.

"You shouldn't have turned the light on, Claire. He could be some kind of crackpot or weirdo and he might try and come and visit us now."

"Oh shut up! That's not funny," said Claire, her stomach turning over at Carol's words.

Carol switched the light off again and told her friend not to switch it back on this time, and she studied the creepy voyeur's window with the binoculars. He was still standing there, but he was no longer looking through the telescope. His face was a pale oval with the dim orange-red light of a glowing cigarette tip in it. After a few minutes he moved away from the window. The light in his room went on, and he reappeared – this time putting on a coat.

"He's going out," said Carol, turning to Claire with a worried expression on her face.

Claire understood exactly what she was thinking. Was the creep really about to pay them visit?

A little over five minutes later, the girls were sitting huddled together in the dark, looking through the window scanning the deserted street below, when a man, aged about forty, came slowly walking along the street, scrutinising each window as he passed. It was him – the telescope man.

Claire suppressed a little scream and retreated from the window, but Carol stayed put. The man stopped directly beneath their window and stood there for a few moments.

"Get away from the window," Claire whispered to Carol. "He'll see you."

Carol shuffled backwards a few feet but brushed against the curtain, betraying her presence.

"Hello," came the man's voice weakly from the street below.

"He's seen you now, you stupid cow."

"What are we hiding for anyway?" said Carol, who had always been much bolder than her friend. "It's our flat and he can't get in and if he tries anything we'll call the police."

"Even though we don't have a phone," Claire said, sarcastically.

"I'd scream this place down if he tried anything," Carol reassured her.

Then something hit the window with a click, and it bounced off the ledge outside.

"He's throwing stones up, the cheeky sod!" said Carol, furious.

"Just keep away from the window, he looks away with the mixer," Claire urged her with a tremble in her voice.

Then another stone, a much larger one this time, hit the windowpane with a loud crack.

"That's it!" said Carol and she flung open the window and unleashed a string of four-letter expletives at the stranger. Throughout it all he tried to speak and kept shaking his head. Eventually she paused long enough for him to say, "Look, I know you must think I'm some perverted peeping Tom, but I wasn't looking at you and your friend in the way you think I was," pleaded the man in a soft, well-spoken voice.

"Well what the hell were you looking at us for then?" Carol shouted down at him, as Claire tried to drag her from the window.

"I was looking at the ghosts," came the strange reply.

Carol turned to Claire with a mystified expression, then turned to look back at the odd man, and with a false laugh, she asked, "You what?"

After a short pause the visitor said, "I know this sounds ridiculous, but I can see ghosts. I'm psychic."

The girls, who usually had an answer for everything and could hold their own with the best of them, were stunned into silence.

The man continued, "And I noticed two men ... two ghosts ... in your flat. At first I thought they were your partners, but when I saw them disappear and walk through the walls of your flat, I realised what they were."

Carol swore at the man, called him a nutter and a psycho, and warned him to go away, as she was going to call the police. She slammed the window shut, turned on the light, and after a few minutes peeped through a gap in the curtains. The street was empty – the man had gone.

That night, Carol lay in bed, tossing and turning, unable to sleep. A strand of light from the lamppost in the street illuminated half of Claire's face as she lay in the other bed, and Carol could see her friend's long eyelashes occasionally blinking. She was still awake too, and probably worrying about what that crank had said about the ghosts.

"Be funny if he had seen something," Claire said suddenly.

"Oh! don't say that."

Carol turned and looked at the faint green luminous fingers of the clock. It was almost 2.40am.

"I'm just kidding," said Claire. "We've lived here now for nearly a year and we've never seen any ghosts, have we?"

"No," said Carol.

Then she remembered something. One evening, at around 11 o'clock, a few months ago, she had been drifting off to sleep when she thought she felt the mattress move. It had actually jolted quite violently, but she hadn't been sure if she had been dreaming. Then Carol's mind became her biggest enemy as she lay there in the dark, because she suddenly recalled another strange incident.

"Claire?"

"What?"

"Do you remember, about a fortnight ago, when I had insomnia and palpitations?" Carol asked.

"Yeah."

"Well, I could have sworn I heard someone making a noise that night, like a sigh, right here in this room," said Carol, "and that's what was stopping me getting to sleep."

"Oh, thanks for that," Claire said, looking over at her. "That's a nice thing to tell me at this time in the morning."

However, the girls did somehow manage to get to sleep, and the next morning they vowed never to talk about ghosts, or the supernatural again. They liked their little flat and didn't want anything to spoil living there. After his visit that night they rarely saw the peeping Tom at his window in St George's Heights.

Months later, on Halloween, Carol and Claire invited an old school-friend named Donna over to their flat, because she had quite a reputation for being a good Tarot card reader. Donna had been bullied at school because she claimed that she could see things that no one else could. So serious was the bullying, that she suffered a nervous breakdown when she was fifteen, and the Donna whom Carol and Claire had known at school was not the same Donna who had emerged on the other side of that breakdown. She lost a lot of her friends after undergoing that drastic personality change.

Donna was rather uncommunicative when she arrived at the flat, and as she read the Tarot cards, Carol and Claire could hardly hear her interpretations, because she spoke so quietly. Just an hour after she had arrived at the flat, she suddenly jumped to her feet and declared that she had to go, and left, without further explanation, in a very agitated state.

Two days later, a letter arrived at the flat while Claire was all alone. As she read the missive she felt icy ripples running down her spine. The letter was from Donna, and in it she said:

Please leave that flat. There are two evil spirits with you. As I was reading your cards, one of them realised I could see him, so I had to pretend I couldn't see him, but he knew I could, and he said if I told you two about him he'd kill me and keep me as his slave in the afterlife.

One of the spirits is from a long time ago, from the 1940s I think. He was killed in a house that stood on the place where your flat is. A bomb fell on the house and killed him. The other spirit is of a man who was very evil when he was alive. He died after he drank something he'd put poison in. He had intended to poison a girl with the drink but drank it himself by accident. He puts his hands inside of your body at night as you sleep to try and stop your heart.

Before she had had time to fully digest the contents of the letter, Claire suddenly sensed an ice-cold presence behind her. The iciness spread over her left shoulder, as if something deathly cold was reading that letter from behind her. She dashed out of the living room, through the hallway, and seized the doorknob of the front door – but she couldn't open it. The coldness came rushing towards her from down the hall like an arctic blast. Claire looked down at the bolt on the door, and saw that it was drawn back. So what was stopping the door from opening? She uttered two words – "Jesus Christ" – and that door suddenly budged. She wrenched it open and flew down the stairs, panting, "Oh my God!", over and over until she reached the safety of the street.

She walked in a daze to her mother's home in Tuebrook and telephoned Carol, who was at work at a shop on Leece Street. She told her about the letter and the terrible icy cold thing she had felt on her back and neck, and that she was now going to live at her mother's home and had no plans to return to the haunted maisonette. Carol sent her two brothers to the flat to salvage her and Claire's belongings and after a short period living with their respective parents the two girls went to live at another flat in the Dingle.

To this day they both shudder whenever they think about the time they cohabited with two evil spirits.

ZOMBIE

In the early 1930s, a mysterious and handsome Haitian gentleman arrived at Liverpool and he went by the distinctive name of Josué Beauchamp. He spoke French, Creole and perfect English. He always wore a bowler hat, a finely-tailored, cedar-coloured suit and silk waistcoat, and carried a hickory walking cane with a silver handle fashioned as a skull.

The source of Mr Beauchamp's wealth was not known, but soon after his arrival in the city he bought a house on Pitt Street, between the purlieus of Chinatown and the fringes of a black ghetto, and his multicultural neighbours soon discovered that the man from Haiti possessed unearthly as well as earthly talents. Dark rumours circulated about the peculiar decorations inside his home. Beauchamp had painted the walls of his residence black, and white candles burned after dark at a Voodoo altar. Strange drumming sounds emanated from the house at night, and upon the nights of the full moon, the drumming was accompanied by weird chanting. Then there was Beauchamp's well-witnessed hypnotic seduction of women from every walk of life. These women invariably came to visit him in the evening, and some were reputed to be the wives of well-to-do men across the city.

One night, gunshots rang out on Pitt Street, and a car was seen racing away from the scene of the shooting. It was later established that a rich cotton merchant, Asketh Challinor, had hired a gunman to kill Josué Beauchamp because the Haitian had been having an affair with his young wife, but the gunman had merely grazed Beauchamp's arm.

That same week something terrifying occurred which was witnessed by many people, including several detectives and officers of the law. A muscular black man in his thirties was found dead in mysterious circumstances on Great George Street. One version claimed that he had fallen down the stairs drunk, and another that he had hanged himself. What is known is that Mr Beauchamp ordered the corpse to be taken to his home on Pitt Street. That body was reanimated by a Voodoo spell and by the administering of a potion to the corpse. This concoction consisted of a mixture of herbs, psychoactive drugs and chemicals, mingled with fresh chicken blood.

The dead man rose up from the table, alive, but with a vacant face, devoid of all animation. The corpse had been turned into a zombie, a mindless automaton who can eat, and drink, hear and see, but cannot feel. It had no memory, or any notion of what it was, or who it had been, but nevertheless possessed terrific strength.

The black goliath stood before Beauchamp – who was in fact a bokor – a supreme Voodoo sorcerer. The zombie's eyes bulged white and expressionless as he stood there in the thrall of an ancient West African black magic spell. Under the supernatural guidance of Beauchamp, the dead man walked out into the night. When he arrived at his destination – a house on Belvidere Road, near Princes Park – he smashed through a door and ascended the stairs to the bedroom of a terror-stricken Asketh Challinor, who managed to narrowly escape the clutches of the zombie by jumping out of a window. The cotton merchant sought refuge in the neighbouring house of a friend for a while, before telephoning the police. The zombie tracked him down and was soon hammering on the door of the house. Incidentally, it is said that within months of this terrifying incident, Challinor's hair turned white and the cotton merchant suffered a heart attack one night after screaming out in his sleep.

The police arrived from Lark Lane, but four burly officers could not restrain the frightening specimen of the walking dead. Reinforcements arrived, and they resorted to battering the ghastly looking stalker with riot batons, and such was the ferocity of the onslaught upon the zombie, that one rosewood baton broke in two on its skull. A dozen policemen were eventually needed to subdue what they assumed to be an unusually resilient but insane man and took him into custody, but they soon realised that they were not dealing with a human at all. Their frightening captive gave off choking aromas of decomposition, and vile black fluid dribbled from his mouth in a constant stream. Handcuffs were put on the animated corpse, but the zombie snapped them as if they were made of tissue paper, even after they had dug into the rotting flesh of his wrists.

The police, acknowledging that they were out of their depth with their captive, procured the services of one Alaric Romaine, a well-known psychic detective and occultist based in Rodney Street who has featured in my books before. Romaine quickly informed them that they were dealing with a zombie, and warned them to treat the matter very seriously.

Under Romaine's guidance, the creature was taken (in chains in some accounts) to the Princes Dock Mortuary, and there Romaine filled the zombie's mouth with salt, sewed its lips shut, and had the corpse interred in a coffin bound with chains and buried in a specially designed grave in Toxteth Park Cemetery.

As far as I know, that creature is still at rest there.

In the past I have discussed this case with other students of the paranormal and some have said that it was probably all down to some form of localised mass hysteria, but I'm not so sure, and I have discovered from own research that a midnight burial did indeed take place at the cemetery on Smithdown Road around the time of the incident.

And what happened to Josué Beauchamp, the instigator of this mischief? Well, he changed his name and lived in the city for many years. They say he never seemed to age, and fathered many children by various beautiful women in Liverpool, London and Amsterdam. All of his children were said to have unusually dark eyes, and each of them gravitated towards occultism and the powerful dark practices of Voodoo.

There was a little tale related to me many years ago in the 1980s about one of the descendants of Beauchamp; another colourful character.

A small dog was knocked over and killed on Upper Parliament Street one evening, and the pet's owner, a boy of about nine years of age, was seen kneeling over the poor animal's body at the roadside, crying out loudly and trying to stroke it back to life. An outlandishly dressed black man in his forties arrived upon the scene, bent down and examined the dog, and then poured liquid into its mouth from a small bottle. A crowd assembled around the man, who took after his ancestor in that he was dressed in an exotic manner and was wearing a fez. The crowd crouched down at the roadside to get a better look, but they jumped back in surprise when the dog opened its eyes, and its tail began to wag. Although it still looked weak and wobbly, it was definitely alive. The boy was delighted and thanked the quaint-looking stranger, who patted his head, then walked away towards Earle Road without saying a word.

VISIONS OF FUTURE HORRORS

On the evening of Saturday, 7 October 1933, a glittering twenty-first birthday party was being held at the palatial Childer Thornton mansion of a wealthy businessman, Albert G Wade. Amongst the guests celebrating Elizabeth Wade's landmark birthday, was a chartered surveyor from Hooton named Frederick Garrod, accompanied by his fiancée Helen Meadows, a cousin of Mr Wade. Fred Garrod was introduced to the Wolfs, a Jewish couple who had recently moved to Cheshire from Germany, and they talked about such diverse topics as the property market, the London Stock Exchange, and the outrageous film 'King Kong' which was the film of the moment.

In the midst of the conversation, Fred Garrod was offered a drink which he took to be wine, but felt quite strange almost immediately after drinking it. When he examined the label on the wine bottle he learned that it was Vin Mariani – a controversial Bordeaux wine containing cocaine. The musicians in the room were playing 'It's Only A Paper Moon', but the melody began to sound strange to Fred Garrod's ears, and the room started to sway subtly. Fred looked through the window at the full moon, and watched in disbelief, as its familiar features metamorphosed into a demonic grinning face. Helen could plainly see that there was something wrong with her fiancé and she asked him how he was feeling. Was he ill?

"No, dear. That wine has gone straight to my head. That is all," Fred explained, attempting a smile.

"Then it's soda water for you, darling," Helen told him, and guided her unsteady, light-headed boyfriend back towards the small talk.

When Fred glanced over at the Wolfs, he saw a curious sight. The two of them were wearing striped pyjamas, and Mr Wolf even had on a matching striped flat cap. He drew Helen attention to the bizarre-looking outfits, but she couldn't see any such striped attire. When Fred Garrod took a second look at the Jewish guest and his wife, he was bewildered to see that the couple's clothes had returned to normal.

On the following morning, Fred awoke with a pounding headache, and he frowned with pain as he and his fiancée travelled by train to her mother's home on Fisher Drive, Southport, where a very strange incident took place. In the afternoon, Fred Garrod experienced an ominous sense of foreboding; a conviction that something really dreadful was about to happen. Helen and her mother watched him tremble, but Fred tried to assure them that he was just suffering from the after effects of the odious Mariani wine. Then he noticed a faint whistling sound coming from the sky somewhere above the house.

"What's that?" he cried, gazing up at the ceiling with an expression of trepidation.

Helen couldn't hear the sound, but Fred put his hands over his ears as he heard the whistle turn into a scream which got louder by the second, and he suddenly felt an irresistible urge to get out of the house. He grabbed Helen by the wrist and dragged her towards the door, but it was too late – something had already smashed into the house. Fred collapsed on the floor and felt the house shudder violently. He heard the ceiling caving in and the walls collapsing. When he looked up though, it was obvious that the residence was perfectly intact, and Helen was leaning over him with tears in her eyes and her mother was imploring her to call for a doctor.

Thankfully, as the days wore on, the strange visions and unexplained sounds faded away until Fred's life returned to normality.

Many years later, of course, World War Two broke out, and that very house on Fisher Drive was bombed shortly after an air raid on Liverpool. Somehow, Fred Garrod had glimpsed one of these attacks back in 1933, seven years before the Luftwaffe – Hitler's angels of death – flew over the North West.

Years after that twenty-first birthday party at Childer Thornton, Mr and Mrs Wolf had returned to Germany to visit relatives when they were rounded up with other Jews by the Nazis. The Wolfs ended up in a concentration camp, and would have been forced to wear the striped camp uniform which resembled pyjamas, such as was worn at the notorious Auschwitz camp. Could this have been the bizarre clothing which Fred Garrod saw the couple dressed in at the party years before?

THE THING FROM THE LOOKING GLASS

Most human beings are so preoccupied with the trivialities of everyday living, that they rarely think about such abstract concepts as dimensions. It seems obvious to the mathematically minded amongst us that the space we occupy has three dimensions, so that every physical object has length, breadth and depth, but it is a scientific fact that there are even more dimensions than the ones we are able to perceive. Just as we and a myriad of life forms, ranging from tiny sub-microscopic viruses to the twelve-tonne African bush elephant inhabit this world of three spatial dimensions, it would seem that a variety of creatures abound in the higher dimensions of space and time as well.

A case in point is the strange 'thing' that was seen to partially emerge from a mirror in a student's flat on Princes Avenue, Toxteth, in the early 1970s. Over the years I have had many letters and emails from people who have had very odd and frightening experiences in the premises at this address.

In 1972 a student named Richard was sitting at a desk in the corner of the living room of the flat when he saw the old mirror on the wall in front of him suddenly darken. Then a hideous, green, octopus-like creature with writhing tentacles started to appear, and understandably, Richard bolted from his desk and ran downstairs to summon his landlady – but she had a very jaundiced view of students and assumed that her lodger had taken LSD or some other hallucinogenic drug. However, suddenly, there was a loud crash upstairs and the landlady decided to take a look at the flat for herself. She noted that the mirror seemed normal enough, but was hanging crookedly. The student's desk, however, had been overturned and his papers were scattered across the room. Richard was so shaken by the experience that he took up lodgings elsewhere at the earliest opportunity.

A young couple named David and Sandra then moved into the Princes Avenue flat, and within days strange things began to take place. Sandra woke up one night and left her bed to go to the toilet, but on the landing she found herself enveloped by impenetrable darkness. She put her hand in front of her face and saw it as a dim ghostly outline. The girl naturally became frightened and tried to feel her way along the walls of the landing, but felt nothing. It was as if she was within a vast, pitch-black hall, and when she shouted for her partner, her cries echoed accordingly. Then she felt something ice-cold and snakelike curling around her right knee. To her left, she could also hear laboured breathing, coming heavily in long gasps, and it didn't sound human.

As abject terror gripped the twenty-two-year-old, she watched as a long rectangle of light appeared in the dark void, and she tried to make her way towards it but felt as if she was walking in quicksand. Then the familiar form of her boyfriend David suddenly appeared in the bright yellow rectangle, which was now recognisable as the doorway of the bedroom and Sandra found herself back on the solid floor of the landing. She started to sob, and David hugged her and asked where on earth she had been for the past half-hour. He had searched everywhere after realising she was not in the toilet. Sandra told him about her terrifying experience, but he thought she had merely been sleepwalking, even though he could see that she was deeply traumatised.

Upon the following day, at around 3pm, David was reading a newspaper in the living room when some slight movement caught his eye. He glanced up to find an enormous greyish-green object in the mirror, staring at him with a pair of ghastly, inhuman eyes. He leapt out of the armchair, yanked open the door and bounded down the steps and out into the street. When Sandra returned from shopping, she found him quivering at the corner of the street in a pitiful state. What he had seen made him view Sandra's experience of the night before in a new light and he complained to the landlady that the place was haunted and that they'd had enough. They were not prepared to spend another night in the flat and so they moved out that very day. However, the haunting of the flat on Princes Avenue continued with the next unsuspecting tenant.

The year 1972 will be remembered, by those who lived through it, as a turbulent time of industrial strikes, the IRA bombings of mainland Britain, the three-day week, airplane hijackings, the Women's Lib movement, an inept Government, and power-cuts brought on by a national coal strike. One evening, in the winter of that year, a power-cut struck Liverpool and plunged the flats of the haunted house on Princes Avenue into darkness. Maureen Kelly, one of the tenants of the troubled house, rushed to light the candles she had bought earlier that day in anticipation of a power cut. Maureen was living alone at the flat after separating from her husband, who had acquired the habit of hitting her every time he came home from the pub drunk. Her children were terrified of their violent father and were being looked after by Maureen's mother in Kensington until she could find a suitable house where she and her

51

kids could live in peace, as far away as possible from the wife-beating drunkard.

Maureen's flat was adjacent to the flat that had been vacated twice by tenants because of alleged supernatural goings on, but Maureen was a down-to-earth woman who didn't believe in ghosts, and she never really paid much attention to the strange stories that other lodgers had told her about the haunted apartment next door. She certainly hadn't seen or heard anything strange. However, all that was about to change that winter evening as Maureen sat listening to an old battery-operated Dansette radio for some company. It was tuned in to Radio Luxembourg, and her favourite pop song was lifting her spirits somewhat. Three candles flickered around the room, and one of them suddenly cast an enormous shadow of something terrifying and unfamiliar on the wall. It looked like some kind of creature with writhing tentacles. Maureen turned, with her heart pounding, but saw nothing, even though the shadow was still being cast by whatever it was. She wondered if a spider suspended from a thread was casting the frightening shadow, but couldn't see one. The shadow suddenly flitted across the room and then vanished, leaving Maureen feeling very uneasy.

She sat there in her curlers for a while before deciding to go out to the local pub at about 9pm, just to escape from the spooky atmosphere of the candlelit flat. The station on the radio drifted away, and Maureen was thumbing the tuner wheel when she suddenly heard a floorboard creak behind her. She turned the radio's volume right down and froze. Her eyes glanced about for a weapon with which to defend herself against the intruder, when she heard a peculiar rasping sound. Something cold and heavy slid over her shoulder. Maureen started to whimper as she realised that the thing was a tentacle of some sort. "Jesus Christ!" she cried out, and the thing behind her repeated the phrase, parrot fashion, in an unearthly voice. Maureen flung the door open and ran screaming down the stairs in her bare feet and out into the street.

An old man, Mr Dewhurst, who had once lived at a flat in the Princes Avenue house, found Maureen in a distressed state on nearby Selborne Street, and when she told of her bizarre experience, he didn't doubt her, as he too had heard many strange stories about the flat when he lived in the house.

Tony Price, a local ghost-hunter, investigated the case and discovered that sightings of the 'thing' had been reported since 1968. Tony was something of a freethinker amongst ghost investigators, and he believed that the entity was either

52

trapped between dimensions, or was deliberately intruding on our dimension through some weak point in the barrier which separates it and another space-time continuum. He left a sound-activated tape recorder in one of the rooms and captured the eerie sound of something talking in an unknown language.

In the end, Tony concluded that the mirrors in the flat were acting as portals for the tentacled creature, and he advised the landlady to remove them. This was done, and the 'thing' was never seen again.

WHITE TOP

It was close upon midnight, and a warm summer moon hung low over the seven hills of Liverpool that night in 1893. At a sumptuously-furnished apartment off the south corridor of The Albany building on Old Hall Street, four Lancashire men in their fifties and a thirty-two-year-old man about town by the name of John Magennis, were gathered around an old Georgian mahogany card table playing poker. Small talk and random trivia from the younger player punctuated the tense progress of the game.

"If you add up all of the numbers on a roulette wheel, the total is six-hundred and sixty-six, the Biblical Number of the Beast," said Magennis, who was seated on the edge of a piano stool. The four men didn't react, such was their concentration. "When I served in India, I was almost court-martialled for playing baccarat in the Taj Mahal," Magennis continued, stubbing out a cheroot in the overflowing ashtray. He then presented the highest-ranking hand in poker – the Royal Flush. "Ace, King, Queen, Jack and a Ten!" the young card-sharp proclaimed. Triumphantly, he laid out the winning hand on the tabletop and looked up to see the oldest player, fifty-seven-year-old George Magee, pointing a derringer pistol straight at him.

"Don't take us for fools, Mr Magennis," he hissed in a low gruff voice. "We've been watching you, you scoundrel. You switched our pack for a deck of marked cards. Put your hands up, or I'll put you in lavender."

For once, Magennis's cockiness drained away from him, and he was rendered speechless. Another player searched him and quickly uncovered the incriminating pack of cards, along with a pistol.

"I've played this game in Texas, where they shoot people like you, Mr Magennis," Magee told him, and the young cheat began to visibly perspire.

A player named Robert Nickels suggested calling in the police, but Magee had other plans. To the three honest players he said, "White Top?" and they returned looks of shock and astonishment. The charlatan Magennis had no idea who, or what, White Top was, but the four older men knew a little about this legend of the gaming world, and George Magee knew more than most.

White Top was a brilliant mathematician, who had abused his phenomenal faculties of computation to become the greatest gambler in the world, and he had earned his strange nickname because of the white top hat he always wore, and which had become his trade mark. Under one alias he had broken the bank at the Monte Carlo casino with a sophisticated system based on his abstruse theory of probability, and under another assumed name, in the United States, he had fleeced the riverboat gamblers along the Mississippi from St Louis to New Orleans. Some said he once pitted his skills against the Queen's premier card-player with the Crown Jewels at stake – and won – but being an ardent Royalist, he refused to take the monarch's regalia, and instead accepted an IOU for a tenth of their value.

Nowadays, White Top lived in a grand mansion set in three hundred acres of land, somewhere in the north of England, and here he had become bitter and twisted with the type of dangerous boredom which too much wealth often brings. White Top's men sought out the greatest gamblers and either abducted them, or lured them to his palatial home under false pretences, and there they were forced to play games of chance with their very lives as the stake. This was to be the fate of the card shark John Magennis.

And so, in the early hours of Saturday, 19 August 1893, George Magee marched the card cheat John Magennis out of the Albany on to Old Hall Street with the barrel of his double shot derringer pistol pressed firmly into the young gambler's back. Two of Magee's friends flanked Magennis and a third strode in front of him. To the poker cheat's right, walked Robert Nickels, and in his side coat pocket he held the pistol he had seized from Magennis.

At the kerb, about fifty yards down the street from the Albany, a four-wheeler carriage stood at the cab stand. The bowler-hatted old cabman was talking to the driver of a hansom cab as he patted the neck of his bay mare. The carriage was soon hired by Magee and the driver told to proceed to a farmstead in the vicinity of Prescot, just over eight miles distant. At this rural destination, the gentleman and the double-dealing Mr Magennis called upon the house of a farmer named Goodwin, a friend of Magee's. The party stayed at the house until 8am, when Magee and Nickels force marched a blindfolded Magennis at gunpoint across the morning mist shrouded fields – towards a row of trees. Magennis by this time was a nervous wreck, having prepared himself for the worst case scenario, and was now convinced that the men he was walking with were going to shoot him at any moment.

He knelt down in the corn stubble and cried, pleading for mercy by saying that he had a wife and family, but old Magee roughly ordered him to get back on his feet and walk on. Beyond the trees the trio came upon a long, well-kept, eight-foot-tall hedgerow that encircled the beautifully landscaped acres surrounding a magnificent country house. Magee cautiously opened a gate set in the middle of the hedgerow and he and Nickels pushed Magennis through the entrance, which led immediately into an incredibly convoluted maze. Magee knew that the key to successfully negotiating the maze was to keep one's left hand on the left side of the hedge at all times. Eventually they emerged from the maze and came face to face with a man sitting in a sentry box with a rifle by his side and a loaded crossbow – pointing their way!

"Shard-a-low," called Magee, with his hand on his chest, and the password saved his life.

The three men were allowed to continue up a straight path, passing curious hedge sculptures featuring hearts, clubs, diamonds and spades.

"Mm, very fitting," smiled Magee.

The blindfold was finally removed from Magennis's eyes, and he immediately beheld the splendour of the white stuccoed, three-storey house with nine bays, a top balustrade, and a grand pedimented stone portico, with Corinthian columns and pilasters set against the walls. At the windows on each end of the facade, guards with crossbows were visible, and they were watching the three men like hawks as they advanced down the path to White Top's majestic residence.

Magee rapped three times on the front door and after a few moments, a traditionally dressed butler answered. Magee muttered something to the butler, and turned to point at Magennis. The butler nodded solemnly and stood aside. Magee beckoned to his friend Nickels and he pushed Magennis into the house. In the marble-floored hallway, there stood a coffin on a bier. Magee and Nickels assumed a family funeral was imminent and felt awkward, but then the doors of an immense drawing room opened, and out came White Top in a cerulean satin kimono, a monocle at his eye, and a morning newspaper folded under his arm. He slapped his hand on the coffin and in a matter-of-fact way said, "His life was his stake in last night's poker game, and the poor fellow lost," which did nothing to help John Magennis' nerves.

Later that morning, sharp as vinegar, White Top was winning round after round of the poker game. As usual, his superstitious beliefs meant that he wore his immaculate white silk top hat as he sat facing the horrified card trickster John Magennis at the small, baize-topped table. Five poker rounds per set, and two sets in all would be played. If Magennis won, he would be taken blindfolded back to Liverpool as a free man, and if there was a draw, then a duel between the two players would settle the score. However, if Magennis lost, he was to be put up against a wall and executed by the crossbow men.

"You play well, Mr Magennis ..." conceded sixty-year-old White Top, cleaning his monocle with a handkerchief, "... but you lack concentration."

"Wouldn't you have trouble concentrating if you knew your life was at stake, sir?" asked Magennis, dabbing at the beads of perspiration which kept popping up on his forehead. His right bottom eyelid twitched incessantly, as he turned to glance at the armed guard at his back.

With an air of annoyance, White Top shuffled the cards and said, "My life has been at stake more times than I can remember at spiels all over the world. That's true gambling, and it adds an exhilarating dimension to the game, don't you think?"

Magennis's mouth was too dry to answer and instead he tried to summon all his powers of concentration to somehow try and beat his loathsome opponent.

The first set was a disaster for Magennis, with the Top winning the last round of the set with a Four of a Kind hand. Magennis was told there would be a break for a walk in the grounds followed by lunch. Then the second set would commence.

Magennis was allowed out unaccompanied into the vast gardens, and during his stroll he sneaked furtive glances towards the crossbow men at the windows who were watching his every move. Two more guards looked out from grass-green sentry boxes at each end of the garden. Then he spotted the gardener, a black man of about fifty years of age. He looked familiar. Surely it couldn't be ... but yes it was. It was Roulette, a legendary casino gambler and card player extraordinaire. He could make a pack of cards stand up and talk, gamblers would quip, but Roulette had vanished into obscurity three years before.

Out the side of his mouth, with his gaze averted from Magennis, Roulette told him not to make conversation. He gave a garbled account of how he had lost a poker game to White Top, but instead of losing his life, he had been forced into the humiliating role of gardener. Roulette told him that the duels White Top had with players were fixed, as blanks were always loaded in the other player's pistol. There was also a marksman with a rifle hidden behind a curtain, just in case the Top missed, or merely wounded his opponent. Roulette flicked a single brass-cased bullet he had hidden away for three years at Magennis. It landed at his feet. He looked around, then casually pretended to brush his shoe with his fingers as he picked the bullet up. Before he could thank Roulette, White Top approached and announced that lunch was ready.

Each of the five poker games in the next set were won by Magennis. White Top was furious, and called him a cheat, for this was truly unheard of. Without more ado, Magennis was taken down to a long room with an eighteen-foot-long table in the centre. At each end of the table there was a pistol. White Top picked up his pistol and instructed Magennis to go and pick up his weapon at the other end of the table.

"You may have first shot" cried the Top, as Magennis surreptiously removed a blank from the revolver's chamber and inserted a live round. He raised the gun and shot White Top in one swift movement.

With horrified disbelief and a bullet lodged in his forearm, White Top crawled out of the room where the fixed duel was to have taken place. John Magennis lay flat on the floor under the long table, trembling at the approaching feet of the marksman who had been positioned behind the curtain. The Top's henchman came around the table and aimed his rifle barrel at Magennis' terrified face. Death came swiftly – but not for Magennis. Three rapid shots rang out, and the marksman was knocked backwards by gunfire from the far end of the room. He dropped the rifle with a clatter and fell down dead. Who had shot him? Magennis naturally wondered, then he saw Roulette hurrying down the room, brandishing White Top's Colt 45. He had wrestled it from the wounded gambler in the hallway. Magennis quickly picked up the late marksman's rifle, and Roulette suggested they should make a break for it while they had the opportunity.

"What about the men with the crossbows at the windows?" Magennis queried, as he fumbled with the German-made, bolt-action rifle.

"The Top has summoned them, they're on their way," said Roulette, peering through the curtains at the acres of lawn. He lifted the sash, and he and Magennis jumped down and decided they had little choice but to make a run for it. They headed for the maze, and were just feet away from reaching the entrance when a crossbow bolt struck Roulette, entering his leg behind the knee. He crumpled to the ground in excruciating pain, and Magennis dragged him behind the hedged entrance of the maze, then fired upon one of the advancing crossbow men with the rifle, but missed. Roulette limped along with his arm curled about the neck of the other escapee, and in the confusion, Magennis took a wrong turning in the green labyrinth, and reached a dead end.

"You make a break for it, I'm done for," gasped Roulette, but Magennis, despite being regarded as a trickster and a card cheat, held the legendary black gambler of New Orleans in high esteem, particularly since he had saved his life, and he refused to leave him. He struggled to lead the injured Roulette from the maze – and walked straight into White Top's crossbow men. They escorted Magennis and Roulette back to the mansion, where White Top was being attended by a doctor who had long been struck off the medical register. The bullet had been removed and the Top's forearm was now bandaged. He had been given morphia during the barbaric operation, and now regarded the captured men with glazed, emotionless eyes. The disgraced doctor then removed the bolt from Roulette's leg without anaesthetic and bandaged it. White Top put a single bullet in a revolver, spun the chamber, and handed the gun to Roulette, who was already sweating profusely from his injury. He knew the procedure. He put the gun to his temple and pulled the trigger. A click echoed. He handed the gun to Magennis, who put the gun to his own head. A click. This happened five times, and then it was the turn of Magennis. White Top's lackeys grinned as the card cheat looked at the revolver.

"Unlucky," mocked the Top.

As a last request, Magennis asked if he could take one last look at the picture of his late mother, which he kept in a locket. White Top acquiesced, but when he saw the faded image of the woman, he blinked his sedated eyes and reached for it.

"What was your mother's name?" he asked.

"Violet Charroux," replied John Magennis Charroux. The Top asked him what year he had been born, and the apparently doomed gambler said, "Third of March, 1861". After a lengthy interrogation of Magennis, White Top suddenly took the revolver from his hand and hugged him.

"I thought you reminded me of someone – you're my son!"

It was the luckiest day of John's life.

PHANTOM OVER SEFTON PARK

Strange things are being reported in the skies over Liverpool, and for once, the enigmatic UFO is not to blame, but something rather more sinister: a ghostly woman in flowing white robes. I first received a letter about this aerial apparition in February 2005 from a Mrs Baker, a woman who saw the airborne ghost hovering about 200 feet in the air over Sefton Park one moonlit night as she walked her dogs.

"She came from the direction of Aigburth Vale, and seemed to slow down over the Palm House," Mrs Baker told me when I interviewed her at her Mossley Hill home. She added, "I called my brother on my mobile and he came out thinking it was a wind-up, but then he saw her too. His eyesight isn't as good as mine and he thought it might have been a kite, but who would fly a kite at 11.30pm? I could distinctly see that it was a woman, in what looked like some old-fashioned nightgown. She drifted off towards Brompton House and vanished into the night. I waited in case she came back but she didn't, and I wasn't really scared; more intrigued."

That was not the only sighting of the flying spectre. A few months later I was contacted by Jimmy, a hackney-cab driver, who told me how he and two passengers had been travelling up Ullet Road one evening in March 2005 at about 9pm, when he happened to glance up.

"I couldn't believe what I was seeing," says Jimmy, a devout Roman Catholic. "I saw this white thing in the sky, and at first I thought it was a balloon, and when I tried to look, there were treetops in the way, but as soon I got a better view, I could see that this thing, which was about six hundred yards away, was a person in a long white dress. I drew the attention of the two girls in the back of the cab to the strange sight, and they saw it too. I pulled over and we watched it move slowly downwards through the sky towards Greenbank Park, where it vanished. I was always told that ghosts are spirits that need prayers and I just made the sign of the cross after seeing it. I dropped the girls off near Penny Lane then drove towards Greenbank Park, hoping I could see whatever it was, but I saw nothing."

A few months before these sightings, a security guard who does not want to be named was gazing out from a building which overlooks Sefton Park during his coffee break. A full moon loomed on the horizon, and the guard was studying the lunar orb through a pair of army surplus binoculars, when he suddenly saw something glide beneath the its disk. It was a ghostly pale figure of a woman, wearing, in the words of the guard, "a long white garment, almost like a burial shroud."

Despite feeling quite alarmed, the guard tried to keep his hands steady on the binoculars, and he managed to track the eerie ghost for about thirty seconds as it drifted across the sky.

"She didn't move, she was like a statue," the security officer told me, "and at first I thought I was seeing things, but then all of a sudden, the police helicopter flew over the park, with its searchlight on, and the beam went straight through the woman as it swept across the lake. I was dazzled by the searchlight and when I looked up again I couldn't see her. I'm not ashamed to say that I went cold when I saw her. I'm not sure if the personnel in the chopper saw her. I'm worried it's an omen, because two people in my family have died since I saw her."

If you too have seen the flying phantom of Sefton Park, or anything else of a supernatural nature, please get in touch with me via the address given at the back of this book.

COCK OF THE NORTH

Thereare some fascinating characters in Liverpool's long history about whom we have scant information. They remain shadowy celebrities of street folklore because they were not Lord Mayors, members of the nobility, or wealthy businessmen, and an individual known only as 'Fitzy' belongs to this class of legendary Liverpudlians. All we know is that an extraordinary man, at the advanced age of sixty, became the uncrowned king of street-fighters in Liverpool, and was nicknamed the 'Cock of the North'. He fought a succession of bare-knuckle pugilists, many a third of his age, and left them unconscious, or maimed for life. Like many Liverpolitans, Fitzy was of Irish and Welsh descent, and he lived somewhere off Scotland Road in the 1880s. He was said to be of middle height and not particularly muscular, yet was possessed of an incredible strength and stamina, and had possibly been a blacksmith in his younger days.

One night in the 1880s, the entire population of a street in the north of Liverpool engaged in a riot of fighting. This came about when two women, each from large families in the street, started a slanging match. One accused the other of spreading gossip about her husband, and within minutes the families of the women were at war. Then the neighbours and friends joined in, until the entire street became a battleground. Windows were smashed, people lost their teeth, and one man was almost lynched from a lamppost. Police whistles pierced the air and batons were swung indiscriminately at heads and bodies, but even the forces of law and order were having a difficult job getting the street back under control – that is until Fitzy appeared on the scene. The formidable fighter did not even have to raise his fists; he only had to walk the length of the street and the trouble-causers fled back into their homes. News of the incident spread throughout the neighbourhood and only served to enhance Fitzy's reputation even further.

At a pub in the area called the Morning Star, a bully of a man in his thirties, after listening to the other drinkers singing Fitzy's praises in hushed tones, suddenly stood up and announced that he was sick of hearing the far-fetched stories of the so-called Cock of the North. With that he took off his shirt and started inviting people to feel his biceps, which everyone had to agree were pretty impressive.

Fitzy was sitting in front of a fire just a few feet away and had heard everything that had been said. He stood up, politely introduced himself, and challenged the braggart to bend the poker by the fireplace. The stranger picked up the poker, and after great exertion in which his eyes bulged and his face turned purple, he managed to bend it slightly. Then, without a word, Fitzy took the poker off him and bent it around the boastful stranger's neck, almost choking him. He then pushed him out of the pub into the wintry street and threw his discarded shirt on to the fire amid a welter of laughter. Still saying nothing – his actions had said it all – he sat back down and resumed drinking his pint as if nothing had happened.

On another occasion, in 1893, an old bay horse fell down dead without warning, on Rose Hill, close to the police station, trapping a little child under its body. Police from the Bridewell tried to comfort the child as desperate efforts were made to lift the dead animal. The boy's hysterical mother rushed into a nearby pub and pleaded with the customers to come and help shift the horse. Fortunately for her, one of the drinkers was Fitzy. He rushed to the scene and astounded onlookers by grasping the horse's main and pulling the animal off the crying child. Amazingly, once released, the boy was none the worse for his experience and Fitzy carried him to a confectioner's shop and treated him to a delicious selection of cakes. This did the trick, and very soon the boy had forgotten all about his trauma.

Fitzy became the subject of pub ballads and skipping-rope chants, and, despite his fearsome reputation, hardly a week passed by without a challenge from some upstart, but none succeeded in even injuring the north-ender. After his mother died in her nineties, the urge to fight eventually seemed to leave Fitzy and he kept a low profile in the local pubs and turned to God, even though his physical condition was still as good. He attended church regularly, and in his seventies he was, by all accounts, as fit as a man half his age.

When and where Fitzy died is unknown, but he was someone's great grandfather – perhaps you are a descendant of the toughest man ever to walk Liverpool's mean streets.

COUNT VARGO

There is an ancient anonymous rhyme which runs thus:

Even he who is pure of heart
And says his prayers by night,
May become a wolf when the wolfbane blooms
And the Moon is full and bright.

Werewolves – men and women who have been transfigured into wolf-like creatures – may seem nothing more than the stuff of grim folk tales from the Dark Ages, but long before the time of Christ, there were well-documented reports of sinister human-wolf hybrids being at large. Some of these creatures were said to have been ordinary people transformed through black magic into enormous wolves, or fur-covered bipeds, who nevertheless retain some of their human characteristics. If only these reports were unreliable, sensational products of a superstitious or unbalanced minds; then we would be able to dismiss them. But a majority of the accounts and descriptions of werewolves come from level-headed soldiers, doctors and lawyers.

The ways in which a man or woman can become a werewolf are not known with any certainty, but it was once claimed that eating the wolfbane plant, or drinking from a stream from which a wolf had drunk, would induce the transformation. Then there is the transforming power of the malevolent curse inflicted by those well versed in Occult science. This was thought to have been the case in eighteenth century France, when a libidinous nobleman, Count Getulio Vargo, attacked a beautiful young gypsy woman near the Auvergne Mountains in southern central France. Count Vargo viciously raped the twenty-year-old woman one moonlit night, but he was apprehended by her brothers as he dragged her screaming by the hair through the woods.

The brothers dealt the young nobleman a severe beating and chased him through the woodland. One of the Romany brothers swore a strange curse at the fleeing aristocrat, which seemed nonsensical. In the jinx, the gypsy warned that all of nature would be against the Count; all the animals in the world would turn against him and that he would never rest. The lustful Count laughed nervously as he fled, but thirty minutes later, a woodcutter saw a strange grey-furred overgrown beast, like a wolf, but reared up on its hind legs, watching him from a forest clearing. The beast roared and charged towards the woodman, who dropped his axe in terror and stood rooted to the spot. Thankfully, the gigantic animal – which was larger than a bear – tore past him and closed in on a caped figure who had been running down a nearby lane. This figure was none other than Count Vargo, just five minutes away from his home and safety.

The Count glanced behind him and saw the looming mass of the lupine monstrosity. The beast seized its terror-struck human prey with its huge foaming jaws and shook the Count's body as if it were a rag doll. The woodcutter suddenly regained the power of movement in his legs and scurried off to the sanctuary of his abode, which was little more than a log cabin. As the woodman opened the door to his mountain home, his sole companion, an old Alsatian shepherd dog, bolted past its trembling master and galloped off towards the strange creature attacking the Count. The hound bit the rear of the ravenous beast, and the it reacted by twisting swiftly from the heavily lacerated body of the Count. In one deadly reflexive movement, the grizzled monster tore out the throat of the old Alsatian with its powerful razor-toothed jaws.

The woodcutter watched what happened next from a small gap in the window shutters of his bolted home. The unidentified animal reared up on its hind legs and released a stomach-churning howl which echoed through the mountains. The animal then turned to face the woodman's dwelling, and for one heart-stopping moment, he expected the demonic bipedal brute to come for him, but instead the animal ran off into the forest. The woodcutter refused to budge from the safety of his home until well after dawn, when he finally ventured out wielding a wood axe to survey the carnage. His old dog lay in a wide pool of congealed blood, but Count Vargo was still alive and moaning, despite heavy loss of blood from a neck and chest wound. The woodcutter carried the Count to his wooden shack and then went to the Count's brothers to tell them of the traumatic incident.

With careful nursing, Count Vargo made a miraculous recovery, but a month later, he went missing from his home. During his convalescence the cook had thought it strange that during the past fortnight, the Count had repeatedly asked him to undercook the meat and poultry for his meals. One of the servants had even witnessed Count Vargo, dressed only in his nightshirt, devouring a raw leg of lamb in the pantry during the early hours of the morning. The Counts's brothers surmised that he had been driven temporarily insane by his horrific encounter with the wolf-like monster, so they paid the local villagers to scour the region in search of him, but the missing aristocrat was nowhere to be found. Then one Sunday night, a month later, in June 1764, a bloodcurdling howl reverberated through the nearby Margeride Mountains in the neighbouring district of Gevaudan, and so began a nightmare saga which is still talked about in that part of France to this day. The howling that caused the peasants of Gevaudan to shiver in their beds came from the Mercoire Forest near Langogne. One brave woman who went out to locate the eerie animal came upon a sight which was to haunt her for the rest of her life. She described the animal to the terrified villagers:

It was the size of a cow with a very wide chest, an enormous head and neck, pointed ears that were like erect horns. It's long snout was akin to that of a greyhound, and four long fangs protruded from the monster's mouth, which was foaming. The tail of the animal was long and very thin, and a black stripe ran from the space between the beast's eyes, along its back, down to the tail. It had big claws which looked like a man's hand, only three times larger, and its eyes glinted red and contained so much evil. For as long as I live I shall never forget the malicious way the creature regarded me. Those eyes were not those of an animal; they were the eyes of something that had once been a man.

The woman went on to describe how the strange-looking animal had circled some cows in a field, obviously intent on devouring one of them, but two bulls had kept the creature at bay with their horns. After a few tense moments, the freakish animal ran off at high speed, in thirty-foot bounds.

In the months following the sighting, the 'Beast of Gevaudan' as it became known, went on a killing spree; and humans as well as livestock fell victim to its rapacious appetite. The beast was indiscriminate in its choice of human victim, and slaughtered men women and children in the region and often left them barely alive and minus their torn-off limbs. The people of Gevaudan and the farming communities of the Margeride mountains barricaded themselves indoors as soon as twilight was falling, but the marauding beast still found more victims. One young milk maid was literally torn apart within twenty feet of her two brothers, who attempted to beat off the Beast of Gevaudan with cudgels studded with spikes, but it was useless. The animal seemed invulnerable and hardly reacted to the two men beating it on the head and back, as the screaming woman's head was torn off by its lion-sized jaws. One of the brother's fled in panic and the one who stood his ground had four fingers on his hand bitten off by the Satanic creature. When the brothers returned at first light to the scene of the attack, they found their sister's shredded, headless corpse lying in a pool of blood. It was only recognisable because of the ring visible on the remains of one of her mutilated hands. An old man who visited the site of the butchery trembled and remarked, "This is not the work of a wild animal. It is the work of a werewolf. There were werewolves in these woods and mountains when I was a child, and this is the sort of destruction they wrought." The elderly man's comments struck a chord of terror in the mind's of the people gathering to witness the mutilated remains of the milkmaid.

On 8 October 1764, it was confirmed without doubt that the Beast of Gevaudan was no ordinary animal, when two professional hunters tracked it down and blasted it with powerful muskets from a mere ten paces, enough to kill any known animal stone dead. The Beast dropped as the shots ricocheted off its flesh, but quickly rose to its feet. The hunters reloaded their muskets and moved in closer, convinced that they would be able to finish it off, but after they fired at it again at point blank range, the animal merely fell down for a few seconds, then sprang up again and ran off into the woods. Determined to finish off their prey once and for all and so rid the area of the menace, the hunters reloaded once more and gave chase. The men managed to discharge a further two rounds into the animal, but the Beast of Gevaudan seemed impervious to the musket shot and escaped.

Returning to their village, the hunters assured the terrified locals that the bloodthirsty creature had been fatally wounded and would soon be found dead, but their predictions proved to be wildly optimistic, and underestimated the resilience of the Beast. For, in the following week, even more victims were killed by the demoniacal carnivore, bringing the death toll to forty. The Beast of Gevaudan generated so much mass hysteria with its horrific and audacious attacks, that news of it reached the ears of a Captain Duhamel, who decided to draft fifty-seven of his dragoons into the animal's killing grounds.

Forty men patrolled on foot and seventeen mounted soldiers scoured the countryside after dark, but still the Beast managed to continue its horrifying attacks, right under the dragoon's noses. Duhamel was greatly embarrassed by his lack of success and the boldness of the creature. He also added fuel to the werewolf rumour by declaring that the Beast of Gevaudan suspiciously showed an almost human intelligence, which made him ponder upon it's true nature.

Even when the cracksmen of the dragoons had finally tracked the Beast down and fired repeatedly into its body, it seemed invulnerable and simply loped away without suffering a scratch. This seemed to back up the claims of a deranged local peasant suffering from religious mania, who warned the people of the region that Beelzebub had been sent among them disguised as the Beast, as a punishment for their iniquities. The news of the eerie ravenous animal spread throughout France and the other countries of Europe, and soon every professional and amateur hunter was converging on Gevaudan, spurred on by the promise of a large reward which had been put up by the farmers who were being terrorised by the voracious killer.

King Louis XV was mortified by the failure of the dragoons to kill the Beast of Gevaudan, so he enlisted the services of a man named Denneval who was reputed to be the greatest wolf hunter in Europe. Denneval was said to have killed one thousand two hundred wolves during his career and to have an almost supernatural talent for tracking down animals. The hunter turned up at Gevaudan in February 1765 with six of his best bloodhounds and attempted to track down the Beast, but the dogs soon became quivering wrecks and began to yelp pitifully when they approached the area where the creature had recently been seen.

A month afterwards, the Beast carried out a particularly violent attack on the Denis family of Malzieu. Julienne and Jeanne, the young daughters of Farmer Denis, were looking after the livestock in a field with their sixteen-year-old brother Jacques, when the Beast came out of hiding and struck. Twenty-year old Jeanne suddenly let out a scream which Jacques immediately realised could mean only one thing. Turning from the fire he had just lit in the field, he saw the enormous wolf-like animal seizing his sister's head with its massive jaws. He was so enraged by the animal's attempt to kill his sister, that he ran over to it and somehow managed to grab the animal by its throat and wrestle it away from Jeanne, who was howling hysterically.

Jacques squeezed the Beast's throat as hard as he could, and the animal snapped at him as if he were some pesky fly, but the muscular young farmhand drew on his fear and anger and from somewhere summoned an inner strength. He cast the Beast on to the fire and the animal howled in agony as the flames singed his fur and burnt its paws, then ran off into the forest to lick its wounds.

Jeanne Denis was still screaming with blood pouring from too deep perforations behind each ear, made by the Beast's fangs. Jacques tried to calm his sister down but she never recovered from the attack and went insane.

A month later, the gruesome remains of a woman and her child were found in a wood. The grisly find made Denneval even more determined to track down the creature, but, despite his best efforts, it always seemed one step ahead of him and continued to evade capture.

In April 1765, the Beast approached a nobleman called de la Chaumette and began acting very strangely. De la Chaumette related how the animal had wagged its tail, as if to exhibit some sort of affection for him. It whined and approached the nobleman, who was on horseback, but thinking it was a ruse, he reacted by firing his pistol at the creature. It ran off and kept glancing back before it vanished into a wood. That same day the Beast was seen crossing a ravine just a mile from the curious encounter with de la Chaumette.

Around this time, an old Jesuit priest made a startling accusation about de la Chaumette's placid encounter with the Beast of Gevaudan. He maintained that the Beast had actually been the nobleman's close friend Count Vargo, in the form of a werewolf, and that was why the animal had acted so affectionately towards him. De la Chaumette outwardly pretended to be outraged by the holy man's claim, but secretly confided to friends that the Jesuit might have hit on the awful truth behind the Beast of Gevaudan. After all, no one had yet been able to find the missing Count. The Jesuit was later interrogated by de la Chaumette, who was curious to discover how the Roman Catholic priest had deduced that Count Vargo actually was the Beast. However, the elderly divine would only say that he could no longer comment on his allegation, because his superiors had instructed him to refrain from discussing werewolves and other unholy creatures.

In May 1765, the creature terrorising Gevaudan killed several people in one day and also killed the rumours that the Beast had finally been killed by the troops. The King of France had been confidently informed by his emissary Denneval that the creature had been killed and was probably lying dead in a wood somewhere. When he heard that the Beast was still at large and again on the rampage, Denneval was unceremoniously sacked by the monarch, and Antoine de Beauterne, the King's personal gun carrier was assigned to the task of ridding Gevaudan of its monster.

De Beauterne was more methodical than his predecessors in his pursuit of the

Beast. He drew up detailed maps of Gevaudan, analysed the common routes the animal took on its people-hunting expeditions, and hatched meticulous plans to entrap the creature. All the strategies hinged on a gut feeling he had about a ravine in the area, which he suspected of being the Beast's lair.

By 21 September of that year, the plans had all been formulated and rehearsed to a tee. Forty hunters and a dozen dogs encircled the Beal ravine. The circle of men and canines closed in slowly, and sure enough, the Beast soon appeared in a clearing. It turned slowly, surveying the armed men closing in on him as they beat the thicket with canes. The hunting dogs barked furiously at the unearthly creature, which was looking desperately for a break in the human link to make its escape. Suddenly, the Beast's head went down and it charged at one of the hunters, but Antoine de Beauterne shouldered his heavy calibre musket and fired. The shot blasted the Beast's eyeball open and exited through its skull. Another shot from a gunman struck the animal in its right shoulder. The Beast reared up on its two legs, then toppled to the ground. One of the hunters cheered and sounded on his horn in triumph.

Then the Beast reared up again with blood dripping from its mangled eye socket. It bounded at de Beauterne, but just as it was about to pounce, another hunter shot hit it in its thigh. The animal yelped and turned towards a break in the circle, then raced off to make its escape. Antoine de Beauterne and the hunters watched in disbelief as the ultra-resilient creature once again cheated death and evaded capture, but this time the animal was too seriously wounded, and as it staggered off, it stumbled and fell. It was unable to get up again, and when the hunters gathered around the Beast with their muskets trained on it, they saw, with relief, that the mighty animal was motionless. At last, the Beast of Gevaudan was dead.

Even in death the Beast was an imposing sight; the carcass was measured and weighed and was found to be over six feet in length and weighed 143 pounds. No one could decide just exactly what the animal was, although some naturalists claimed it was simply a rare type of overgrown wolf. The Beast of Gevaudan was promptly stuffed and taken to the King's court for his perusal. It was later exhibited at the Museum of Natural History in Paris, but unfortunately was lost at the beginning of the twentieth century.

The people of Gevaudan regarded Antoine de Beauterne as their saviour, and were almost ready to venerate him as a saint, but in the winter of 1766, something started killing and mutilating the locals once again. The word went round that the Beast had been resurrected, while other rumours had it that there was a family of werewolves at large in the area.

In the summer of that year, several villagers from Gevaudan made a pilgrimage to Notre Dame de Beaulieu, which was located at the foot of Mount Chauvet. After celebrating mass and taking holy communion, the pilgrims produced a gun and several cartridges which they had brought along with them and requested that they be blessed by the priest. When they returned to Gevaudan, a man named Jean Chastel was given the blessed gun and cartridges in order to kill the new Beast.

The slaying took place on 19 June 1767, at the scene of the last Beast-slaying – the Beal ravine. Chastel read out several passages from the Bible, after which everyone present heard the rustling of leaves. An enormous animal, which looked identical to the Beast, burst out of the shadows of the ravine and stood staring at Chastel. The latter raised his blessed musket loaded with the blessed ammunition and pointed it at the creature. After saying, "You will kill no more," he opened fire and hit the animal in the head. The gigantic wolf-like creature fell dead instantly. Some accounts say the second Beast was then thrown on to a bonfire, and that on the spot where it was killed, the grass still refuses to grow.

Count Vargo was never found, but there is a bizarre and frightening legacy of the nobleman-werewolf with a local connection. It is said that during his lifetime as a werewolf, the Count impregnated a number of women – of both peasant and noble stock – and these unfortunate women gave birth to a variety of human-werewolf hybrids. One of these was said to have gnawed its way out of its mother womb, committing matricide before it was run through with a sword. Another of Vargo's offspring resembled a normal baby girl – until the night of the full moon, when the babe's arms and legs became dotted with goosepimples and it would become restless. As the child grew older, it would often get down on all fours and attack the family dog, sometimes inflicting serious bites upon the poor animal. Yet another of his descendants became covered with thick body hair during his teenaged years, and would undergo all types of grotesque metamorphoses when the full moon shone down. In the end the unfortunate wolf-blooded youth hanged himself rather than face a life of lycanthropy and cannibalism.

Shortly after the outbreak of the French Revolution, in 1789, members of a secret society of English aristocrats, allegedly founded by the Prince of Wales, were instrumental in rescuing many condemned French aristocrats from the guillotine. Several members of an aristocratic family were spirited out of France by this secret society during the Reign of Terror – including a countess who travelled with a large locked chest which was carried by her servants at all times. The lady was in deep shock because her twelve-year-old daughter had been guillotined, and so when her rescuers in England saw the countess talking to the locked chest, they assumed that the traumatic sight of seeing her child beheaded had turned her mind.

The noblewoman was indeed mentally disturbed by the trauma, but the chest which never left her sight and which was thought to contain her personal wealth in the form of gold and jewellery, was soon found to hold something much more sinister. It is said that a highwayman on Hampstead Heath intercepted a carriage conveying the countess to a Lord's house. The highwayman carried the chest to his den in Muswell Hill, and when he opened it, he saw found that the large box did not contain money after all, but a small hairy child with pointed ears, who jumped out of the chest as soon as it was opened.

The Highwayman sold the strange creature to a circus, and many years later, when it had grown to become 'the wolfman', the travelling company of entertainers were visiting the city of Chester when their freak star exhibit escaped. The wolfman was never recaptured, and upon the nights when the lunar orb was full, blood-curdling howls could be heard echoing across the Cheshire hills. Livestock was slaughtered by the wolfman, and he was never captured. It is said that he assaulted women from both Cheshire and Lancashire and had sexual intercourse with many of them. These women bore children who seemed human enough until they reached the age of puberty, at which time they changed into wolf-like hominids.

These second generation descendants of Count Vargo might well have been responsible for the legends of the Welsh Werewolf (see *Haunted Liverpool 3*) and the so-called Allendale Wolf, which terrorised a Northumberland town in 1904, and according to the celebrated master of the inexplicable, Charles Fort, that same creature visited Liverpool that year.

In Liverpool, when the Allendale werewolf had visited the city, a priest gave a topical sermon about Nebuchadnezzar the great Babylonian king (mentioned in the Books of Daniel and Jeremiah) who suffered a strange malady after incurring the wrath of God: he was driven from men, and did eat grass and walk on all fours. He grew hairs like eagles' feathers and his nails became like birds claws.

What then, are we to make of these frightening tales? Do werewolves really exist, or are they nothing more than superstitious nonsense? How can we explain the Beast of Gevaudan? More frightening still – could you have a trace of werewolf blood in your veins?

BEDROOM GHOSTS

In the Halewood area of Liverpool, Alison, a twenty-three-year-old woman, had a traumatic supernatural experience which left her an emotional wreck. Alison moved to Liverpool from West Kirby after falling head over heels in love with twenty-five-year-old Craig, whom she had met at the Krazyhouse night club in Wood Street in the summer of 2004. Alison's parents weren't too keen on Craig; he had dropped out of university and was a bit too laid-back and lazy for their liking. Nor did they think too much of his stubble, his scruffy attire, and the four-letter words with which he continually peppered his conversation. He worked at a supermarket, stacking shelves, and the monthly pay-packet he picked up was quickly eaten up by debts which he had accumulated over the past few years.

A few months after he had started dating Alison, she became worried when her period was late, and when she told Craig that she thought she might be pregnant, he turned into a selfish monster. He warned her that she would have to have an abortion or he would leave her. Then he callously told her how, two years back, he had forced his then girlfriend into having an abortion because he didn't want to start paying out for a child.

By this time, Alison had fallen out with her parents because of their continual criticism of Craig, so she felt she couldn't run home to them. Because of the fall-out, Alison's father had stopped putting money in her account each month, and so now she found herself in quite a predicament. She had seen Craig's true colours now and had had enough of her obnoxious boyfriend, and so she decided to leave him. Luckily she soon discovered that she wasn't pregnant after all, and shuddered to think of what would have happened if she had been carrying Craig's child.

Alison got a job in an off-licence to support herself, and moved into a tiny flat over a shop in the Halewood area of Liverpool. Each night after work she would sit alone in her sparsely-furnished flat and try to drive the memories of Craig from her mind. She would look at her mobile phone screen and think about phoning her parents and asking her father to come and get her, but pride always prevented her from pressing that call button. The only light in this self-imposed misery was Hollie, her friend over in West Kirby, who would often call her. However, Hollie had just started dating a new boyfriend, so Alison hadn't heard from her friend for a few days.

One night, Alison got into bed at midnight and started to read a magazine called *Take A Break*, which features true-life drama stories about people from every walk of life. The radio on the bedside unit was tuned to Radio 1, and rain was pattering against the windows. Alison gradually dozed off and slept until two in the morning – when something awakened her. There was someone in her hallway. At first she thought it was the wind rattling the flap of the letterbox, but then she heard the distinct thud of someone's feet by her bedroom door. Her heart somersaulted. This was her biggest fear about living alone – to be confronted by a burglar. The dread of this very situation had played on her mind so much after moving into the flat, that she had taken to sleeping with a nine-inch long carving knife under her pillow.

The handle of the bedroom door was turning.

Alison felt numb as she turned in the bed and searched for the knife's handle. The door opened with a creak as her hand felt and then grasped the handle of the knife. She watched in horror as a foreign-looking man with dark curly hair and an olive-skinned face walked to the foot of the bed. He wore a white tee-shirt and jeans, was about five foot seven inches in height and about forty-seven years of age. His most notable feature was his staring, wild, wide, evil eyes.

Alison swore at him using some of the profanities she had picked up from her days with Craig, but the man just blinked, then gritted his teeth and surveyed her with a look of intense hatred in his eyes.

It is a well documented fact that in many cases where intruders and killers have gained entry into women's bedrooms, the victims have been unable to move because of fear paralysis, but in Alison's case, she was so angry at the idea of this intruder breaking into her home, for whatever reason, be it theft, rape, murder, or all of the aforementioned – she just wanted him dead. She was surprised at her sudden bout of courage; it was almost as if someone much braver than herself had taken control of her body.

She threw back the duvet, stood up on the mattress, then threw herself at the stranger, screaming as she lunged at him with the knife. The man reflexively held up his arms, but the blade stabbed his unguarded chest repeatedly. The first blow felt as if the carving knife blade had glanced off bone. The second thrust sent it deep through the base of his neck. The five further stabs sent the man to his knees, with bloodstains spreading over his white tee shirt. He clutched the end of the mattress and then gurgled horribly as he coughed up copious amounts of vivid red, oxygenated blood. The intruder looked up at Alison, who just stood

75

there in shock with the knife poised for another thrust, should one be needed. She was still numb and her heart was pounding. He then fell face first on to the carpet with a soft thump.

Alison scrambled across the bed and grabbed her mobile phone from the bedside cabinet. She shut the bedroom door and went into the hallway and tried to call the police, but for some reason she couldn't get a signal. This had happened several times before in the flat, and the trick was to go to a corner near the window in the living room where the reception was slightly better. Alison moved into the corner and dialled 999. She promptly got through to the Emergency Services, but the operator's voice started to break up. She decided that she would have to go outside into the street and make the call, but that meant going back into the bedroom to retrieve the front door keys from her bedside cabinet, and also her slippers which were near the corpse.

She felt decidedly jittery as she entered the bedroom, expecting to see blood and guts everywhere. Gingerly, she leant over the bed – only to find that there was no dead or injured intruder there. A stomach-churning sensation almost took her breath away as she wondered if her attacker could have survived the multiple stabbing and was therefore still at large in the flat. She grabbed the carving knife and looked in the wardrobe – there was no one there. Stranger still, there were no bloodstains on the carpet, or bed, or wall. The girl then examined her hands and the old tee shirt she was wearing, but not a single spot or splash of crimson was to be seen anywhere.

Understandably, Alison was utterly perplexed by all this and began to fear for her sanity. She examined the carving knife but it was pristine, not a smear of blood anywhere upon it. She looked at the place on the carpet where the body had been lying just minutes before oozing blood from the different stab sites. What could possibly have become of it? Alison wondered for just a moment if the episode had all been some dream, some nightmare that had overlapped into waking reality for a while after the rain on the windows had awakened her. The sharpness of the memory quickly dismissed the possibility from her mind.

Until the diffused light of dawn ghosted through the closed blinds, Alison sat there with the television and radio on, drinking one cup of coffee after another, and smoking her way through a full packet of cigarettes. She had texted her friend Hollie with a description of the eerie incident, but no reply came until noon the next day. By then, an exhausted Alison was back in her bed, sleeping uneasily with her fist wrapped tightly around the handle of the carving knife.

On the following day, Hollie and Alison met up for lunch at Café 53 on Bold Street. Hollie quickly dismissed the knifing in the bedroom as a particularly lucid dream, and all she wanted to talk about was her new boyfriend Jake, but Alison refused to be silenced and kept going on about the man she was certain she had killed. It had been too vivid to be a dream, so naturally, Alison wondered if that man had been some sort of ghost.

"You've just been under a lot stress, Ali, that's all," Hollie said, sympathetically, "and you really should come back home. Come home with me today."

"No, I can't. This was nothing to do with stress," said Alison, "because I'd been asleep and I could even hear him walking in the hallway. That's what woke me up."

"Look, it's been a dream, stop worrying," was Hollie's advice, and once again she began to talk about Jake, and how he had invited her to meet his parents.

Alison took the hint and dropped the subject of the stabbing of the phantom man. The two friends left the café, did a little shopping at Top Shop and River Island, then parted company at James Street Station. Alison went into work at 5pm and came home at 10.30pm, feeling really exhausted with having had so little sleep the night before. She still felt uneasy in the bedroom when she got to her flat, so she left the bedside lamp on.

Alison soon fell asleep, but around three in the morning she woke up as she turned over in the bed. She looked up towards the door. She didn't know why she did this, but she felt better for doing so, having satisfied herself that there was no one standing there. She adjusted her pillow, sighed, closed her eyes, then yawned. Lying there with her eyes closed, Alison suddenly had the unnerving feeling that someone was watching her. Reluctantly she opened her eyes and looked at the wall to the left of her bed. As well as the bedside light, the light from a sodium lamppost in the street was filtering through the flimsy curtains into the bedroom, bathing the wall with a faint soft amber glow and illuminating the awful patterns in the wallpaper.

All at once, something moved across those patterns. A pair of eyes was watching her. The eyes didn't blink – they simply stared and widened a few times as Alison looked on in disbelief. She shuddered and could feel goose pimples rising up on her arms and legs and a sudden rush of adrenalin coursing through her veins. Then the bedroom door burst open with such force, that it smashed against the side of the wardrobe. That man entered again, stripped to

77

the waist this time – with seven livid stab wounds in his chest and lower neck. Alison screamed as she realised that the carving knife was behind her, under the pillow, and the man was now climbing on to the bottom of the bed.

What happened next was completely surreal. A naked woman with long black hair suddenly rose up from the bed – from the very space occupied by Alison's body, and in her hand she held a long knife. It was Alison's carving knife. She stabbed the man repeatedly and he cried in agony as the woman shouted at him in what sounded to Alison like Italian or Spanish. All the time the nude woman stood on the bed wildly stabbing the man, Alison noticed that she could not feel any movement on the mattress, as if the woman had no weight or substance to her whatsoever.

As before the man fell with a dull thump to the carpet, and Alison dived under the duvet and hoped it was all just a nightmare.

Then silence.

Alison peeped from under the duvet – and there, inches from her eyes, was the pale face of the strange naked woman, and she was smiling at her. Her dark, mad-looking eyes were those same eyes that had stared out of the wallpaper. Alison couldn't take any more and she closed her eyes and pleaded with God to make that woman go away. After finishing the prayer, she ran from the bed screaming uncontrollably and turned on the light. The bedroom was empty. The body of the stabbed man was nowhere to be seen, and yet the carving knife was on the floor at the place where he had been stabbed.

Alison quickly got dressed, and she telephoned for a taxi to take her all the way to West Kirby, sixteen miles away. When the taxi reached its destination, Alison's father paid the cabby and hugged his errant daughter. At first, Alison's parents were worried that she had been taking drugs that morning when she arrived home from Liverpool, because she kept shaking and talking incoherently. However, it soon became apparent that this was not the case. They understood their daughter well, and knew that she was a level-headed girl who was not prone to imagining things. It was obvious that some awful event had upset her, and Alison eventually gave them the full account of the sinister bedroom intruders, but they couldn't explain what she had experienced.

I investigated the case, and interviewed the landlord of Alison's flat. He was an Arabian man, and he admitted that previous tenants of that flat had also experienced strange incidents, including hearing screams in the dead of night, and on several occasions, knives from the kitchen cutlery drawer would be found in the bedroom.

About seven months after this incident, a remarkable coincidence occurred. At Rodney Street, I received a letter from a reader, asking if I knew anything about a haunted flat above a shop in Halewood. It was the very same flat in which Alison had stayed. The author of the letter – a fifty-two-year-old woman called Denise – wrote that on one occasion when she had been living at the flat, she had been awakened at around two or three in the morning by screams. She looked up from her pillow, and there, in the half-light, she was startled to see a naked woman fighting with a man. She noticed that the woman was brandishing a large knife. Denise hid under the blankets, sensing that the figures were apparitions of some sort. When she dared to look up again a few moments later, the man and the woman had vanished.

What are we to make of this unsolved puzzle of the paranormal? Perhaps at some time in the past a woman murdered her husband, or boyfriend, in a fit of jealous rage, or perhaps he was a wife beater who got his just desserts ... perhaps ... Until I know the full facts behind this haunting, it is probably not worth speculating upon the whys and wherefores that lay behind the periodic supernatural re-enactment. I wonder if the ghosts will be at each other's throats again tonight?

GUILTY CONSCIENCES

In the past I have written about the ghosts of murder victims who have haunted their killers and driven them either to insanity, or caused them to confess to their heinous crimes. The following two stories concern such conscience-pricking apparitions.

In the early 1890s, Number 80 Wood Street was a jeweller's shop owned by one Peter Morris, and in 1891 there was a rumour that a female assistant, Mrs Marsh, had been murdered on the premises. She had gone missing, and what is more, a letter which Mrs Marsh had purportedly written to her sister, telling her she was staying with a man in Birkenhead, had unfamiliar handwriting. Furthermore, when the Birkenhead address cited in the letter was checked, it was found to be an empty house. Mrs Marsh was never seen again, and there were dark rumours that the jeweller, or his friend, Roger Williams, had killed her on the premises of Number 80, and had either buried her in the basement, or thrown her into one of the docks.

Not long after the mysterious disappearance, the ghost of Mrs Marsh made an appearance at the jeweller's, and the shop owner Peter Morris even tried to communicate with the apparition, which had a mark on its forehead that looked like a bullet-hole. The manifestation of Mrs Marsh's ghost became a regular occurrence at the shop and seems to have unhinged the mind of Roger Williams, who was one day found cowering behind a gravestone in nearby St Peter's Church. He was wide eyed with terror and babbling incoherently and it soon became apparent that he was hiding from the ghost. He never regained his sanity and was later committed to an asylum.

***

In the 1980s, twenty-seven-year-old Bryan Skillen left his home off Durning Road with the intention of mugging someone. Bryan had lost his job at a garage six months previously after he was caught red-handed stealing from the petty cash box. Since then, Bryan had developed a drink problem and had decided to take the line of least resistance when he wanted money to finance his booze habit. And so, on this warm summer night, at eleven o'clock, he left his home and went in search of someone to knock down for ready cash. Bryan usually mugged people in the Kensington, Toxteth or city centre areas, but tonight he couldn't be bothered travelling too far, as he intended to go to a nightclub with the money from his 'job' as soon as he had acquired it.

He walked down Wavertree Road looking for a potential victim and his eyes soon lit upon an old man staggering out of the Weighing Machine public house, obviously the worse for wear due to drink. He looked such an easy target. I'll just slap him a few times, thought Bryan, no need to punch him or break anything. Easy!

Just when he was about to pounce, a police car came cruising up Marmaduke Street, and quick as a flash, Bryan turned on his heels, produced a cigarette, and lit up. Once the police car had gone, he soon spotted another target at the junction of Tunnel Road and Upper Parliament Street, but was frustrated this time when a fire engine suddenly came upon the scene, the crew jumping down to put out a fire behind an advertisement hoarding. Bryan gritted his teeth with frustration. Realising that his luck was not in that night, he went home and drank a large quantity of rum. He thought about the day he had been caught stealing the money at the garage with deep regret. He fervently wished that he hadn't given in to temptation and stolen those twenty pounds. He hadn't even needed the money, and it had cost him his job and destroyed the trust of his workmates.

It was almost one o'clock in the morning when Bryan went back out to resume his search for a victim. He turned the corner of Durning Road and walked up Picton Road. There was a man of about twenty-five years of age walking down that road ahead of him. Bryan looked about him to check that there was no one else around, and then he crossed the road and followed the man, treading as quietly as he could.

"Excuse me, mate," Bryan said to the man as he drew alongside. "Have you got a light on you?"

The stranger walked on without even looking back.

"You're not getting away as easy as that," Bryan muttered under his breath, and walked a little faster.

The man continued to walk along Picton Road and he too picked up his pace. He wore a grey, cheap-looking suit and had light brown hair.

Just when Bryan was closing in on his target, the man in the grey suit started climbing a low wall. He scaled it athletically, then stood on top of the wall, peering down at the drop on the other side.

Bryan realised that on the other side of that wall was a sheer, sixty-foot drop on to the train-lines of the Edge Hill depots, for that stretch of the Picton Road formed a railway bridge. The youth turned to look at Bryan. He wore thick, pebble-lensed spectacles, and there were streaks where tears had run down each of his cheeks. He then looked down again at the tracks.

Bryan was stunned and confused, and also a little angry. This definitely wasn't his night. His common selfish side told him to walk on and let the man on the wall jump to his death, if that was what he was determined to do, but some infinitesimally-small spark of conscience deep within him told him to talk the would-be suicide down from the wall. Bryan walked past the man – then halted. He looked up the road, and a solitary car was heading his way. He tried to flag the vehicle down, hoping the driver would help him to get the man off the wall, but the car continued on its way without even slowing.

Bryan walked to the wall and looked up at the tearful man.

"You don't want to go and do that. Come on down, mate," he said.

"No thanks," said the man. "There's nothing worth living for now. No one loves me, so life will go on, and the world's better without me."

"Don't talk like that, come down, come on," Bryan said, and he tried to grab hold of the man's ankle.

The stranger rapidly moved away, out of reach, along the top of the wall and perched on the edge, swaying precariously.

"Stay away from me," he said, and his broken voice was filled with great sorrow.

"Have a ciggy, come on," Bryan coaxed, taking out a pack of cigarettes and a lighter. It occurred to him that it was strange to be so concerned about a man who, only moments before, he was ready to beat up for his money.

"I don't smoke, thank you," said the troubled man.

Bryan looked up and down the road and was surprised to find that there was no traffic, as, even at this time in the morning, there were usually some vehicles passing by. He looked back at the man and asked, "What's your name?"

"Martin," said the man, wiping tears from under his glasses with his fingers.

"Okay, Marty. What's brought all this on, mate?" Bryan asked. He puffed on his cigarette and exhaled through his nose; a mannerism he exhibited whenever he was faced with an apparently insoluble problem.

There was no answer from Martin, just sniffles and subdued sobs.

"Look, Martin, whatever it was, it's not worth taking your life for," Bryan argued, and he glanced up and down the road and cursed the boys in blue under his breath. Any other night any number of police cars would be crawling along this road.

"I caught her ..." Martin began, but became too choked up to finish the sentence.

"You what, mate?"

"I caught my girl with someone else," Martin managed, turning to face Bryan. He looked so lost, like a wounded animal, and tears were streaming down his face.

"Okay, so you caught her with someone," Bryan said, and he struggled as he tried to think of what to say next. "Does that ... erm ... does that mean to say that whatever you and your girl had together means nothing now?"

"She was holding hands with him, and she said she loves him."

As he said this Martin looked down towards the railway tracks, glinting in the actinic glare of a mercury vapour lamp.

"That doesn't mean it's over," Bryan said, still feeling out of his depth, adding, "my mum and dad were separated once because my mum ran off with this fellah, but she came back a few months afterwards and now they're inseparable."

"I want to go back to the way we were," said Martin, and he started to sob loudly.

"Martin, don't jump!" Bryan pleaded. "We can be mates if you like."

"I want to go back to when she was mine and we were going to be married." Martin took off his glasses and wiped his copious tears with the sleeve of his jacket.

"I wish I could go back too, but we have to make do with what we have in the present," said Bryan and now the words came easily and were totally genuine. He thought about the mistakes of his own past, and how he was always hankering to go back to redress them.

Then, with no further warning, Martin jumped.

"No o o o ..." Bryan felt numb.

He heard the body hit the ground with a sickening thud. He climbed up on to the wall, even though he had always had a fear of heights, and he lay flat on his stomach on the top of that wall with his heart pounding in his chest as he peeped over its edge. He couldn't see the body. He felt dizzy looking down from such a great height and was frightened of falling. So he climbed down and ran to a telephone call box in a street off Wavertree Road and called an ambulance. He told the emergency services operator that a man had just jumped off the bridge on Picton Road on to the railway lines, and then he went into the nearby park and kept a watch on the spot from where Martin had jumped. An ambulance turned up with its lights flashing and a man got out of the vehicle and climbed on to the wall. A police car arrived moments later, and an officer left the vehicle with a powerful torch and also climbed the wall. He spent some time shining the torch at the tracks below.

Fifteen minutes later, the ambulance moved off without having retrieved the body, and the police car returned to Wavertree Road police station.

Bryan went home baffled. He read the local newspapers each day, expecting to find some mention of Martin's suicide, but it was never reported.

A fortnight elapsed, and late one night, Bryan Skillen left his home and once again set off to go and hunt for a mugging victim in the Wavertree area. The time was 11.20pm, and in a dark cul-de-sac next to the Cambridge pub on Picton Road, he spied a small old man of about seventy-plus years of age, urinating in a corner. Bryan pulled the brim of his baseball hat right down and went over to him. He tapped him on the shoulder, then held the blade of a penknife in front of his face and snarled, "Give me your wallet, or I'll kill you."

The man cowered and gasped, then fainted.

Bryan caught him before he could hit the ground. He rifled through his pockets and quickly located his wallet. All that old man had was twenty-five pounds – two tenners and a fiver – and Bryan took them, then placed him in a nearby skip that was half full of bricks and rubbish. Bryan then walked homewards up Picton Road. He crossed over Spofforth Road and noticed someone heading towards him.

It was Martin.

Bryan went cold when he saw him climb the wall at the exact same spot from where he had jumped two weeks before. He realised immediately that Martin was a ghost, and ran home to Durning Road, his head pounding. He drank a quarter of a bottle of rum but still the chill inside of him remained. The experience deeply affected the mugger, and made him reconsider his life and the depths to which he had stooped. He realised that he should stop wallowing in self pity about the days when he had been in full employment with friends who had trusted him. Bryan felt that Martin had not been able to move on after his death, and perhaps there was a lesson to be learnt from that.

Bryan never went out mugging again after that night. He was so consumed with shame over the mugging of the defenceless old man, that he started to frequent the Cambridge public house, and one evening he spotted the old man at the other end of the bar. Bryan gave the barmaid an envelope containing fifty pounds and told him to give it to him, adding that it was very important.

"Can't you give it to him then?" the barmaid had asked, suspiciously, and Bryan had said he didn't have time because he had to leave urgently. The barmaid duly gave the old man the envelope, and when he opened it, he found the five ten-pound notes and a small piece of paper. On it was a note from Bryan, sincerely apologising for the mugging.

A year later, Bryan had secured a job as a caretaker at a building used by a Christian fellowship group up in Litherland. He met many people from various walks of life at his job, most of them born-again Christians. One member of the group was a policeman who had lived in Wavertree, and he became a good friend of Bryan's. One night, the conversation turned to the subject of suicide, and the policeman stunned Bryan by telling him about the night he had tried to talk down a man from a bridge in Wavertree, but the man had unfortunately jumped anyway. No one knew why he had committed suicide. Bryan enquired if this man's name had been Martin. The policeman said he couldn't remember, as the incident had taken place about five years before. Bryan therefore described Martin; the thick glasses, and the cheap grey suit. The policeman nodded, "Yes, that's the fellow; how did you know?"

Bryan told his story, and the next day members of the fellowship said prayers for Martin, in the hope that he would be released from his earthly ties and thenceforward, rest in peace.

NOTICE OF DEATH

I have had to change various names and places mentioned in this account to ensure the anonymity of the person who related the story to me. In the 1990s, fifty-one-year-old Joyce was working for the Meals on Wheels service, until she started to experience regular severe pains in her pelvic area. Thinking the worst, she visited a doctor, and was referred to see a specialist. It transpired that the pain was from a benign pelvic inflammatory disease, so a hysterectomy was suggested. Joyce had the operation, and spent six weeks of convalescence at her home in West Derby, attended to by her loving retired husband Mike.

Three weeks into this convalescent period, Joyce felt as if she had fully recovered, and couldn't wait to get back to her job with Meals on Wheels, but Mike insisted that she should not return to employment until the six week period was up. Joyce reluctantly agreed, and turned her hand to light gardening. Filling the long hours was difficult, as she was an active woman who liked to be out and about, and in her job she met many people who had become almost family members to her.

One night, Joyce fell asleep and experienced a very unusual and disturbing dream. She was not a person who usually remembered her dreams, but she awoke at five in the morning in a cold sweat from this one. In it, she was reading the obituary pages of the *Liverpool Echo*, and among the grim listings of the recently departed, she found a surname she recognised – Sugnar. In the dream, Joyce read the death notice, which said:

SUGNAR – MARY, March 23rd 1996. (Gone from our lives but not from our hearts) – Love Sandra, Peter and Family.

The paper then faded away into a terrible cold darkness, and Joyce could see and hear soil being shovelled on to the lid of a coffin at the bottom of a gaping six-foot deep hole.

She awoke with a start, sweating profusely. Thank God it was just a dream, she thought, but she was unable to get back to sleep, so she got up without disturbing Mike and went downstairs to make herself a coffee. She thought about the weird dream and the date she had glimpsed in it – March 23rd – that was only three days away. Mary Sugnar was a seventy-five-year-old Croxteth woman to whom she delivered Meals on Wheels. Joyce sincerely hoped that the dream wasn't some kind of bad omen. So that morning she telephoned Mary, just to put her mind at ease. A man answered it. It was Peter Sugnar, Mary's son, and he told Joyce that his mother had been admitted to hospital after falling downstairs at her home. Joyce was stunned, but of course she didn't mention the vivid dream of the obituary pages and simply wished her a speedy recovery.

On the following day, Mary Sugnar passed away. Joyce grabbed the *Liverpool Echo* off the doormat on March 25 and turned to the Family Notices section. Amongst the obituaries she came across the very same words she had seen in her nightmare. She shuddered as she read and re-read those words.

Joyce told her husband, and as usual, he displayed his typical scepticism towards anything of a supernatural nature, and yet he had never known his wife to tell lies. Joyce was a no-nonsense woman with her feet planted firmly in reality. Mike therefore didn't know what to make of his wife's strange dream, and in the end he decided it was merely a case of coincidence.

Two nights later, Joyce once again dreamt that she was reading the obituaries in the newspaper, and this time, her eyes settled on another name that she was unfamiliar with. The first part of the death notice read:

CATERGORM – FRANK, March 27th, 1996. Suddenly at home, aged 54.

The notice gave the time and place of the funeral, and ended with the telling words: *Donations, if desired, may be given to the British Heart Foundation.* On this occasion, Joyce awoke at 8am. Her husband was down in the kitchen, cooking a fry-up breakfast as he listened to the radio. Joyce sat up in bed, going over the details of the dream in her mind. She then got up and found a pen and a writing pad to write those details down. She told Mike about the dream, and he agreed that it was strange, but then voiced concerns that her hysterectomy operation might somehow be behind the dreams. In turn, he blamed the anaesthetic, hormones, painkillers, antibiotics and stress, but Joyce calmly shook her head to each of his hypotheses.

Instead, she went to the telephone directory, thumped it down on the kitchen table, and searched for any Catergorms – a very unusual name and one she had never heard of before. She soon found that there was a Frank Catergorm living in Mossley Hill.

"That's got to be him, Mike," said Joyce, tapping her finger on the page of the directory and copying down Mr Catergorm's telephone number.

"Please tell me you're not going to call him?" Mike said, with a look of total disbelief. Then he smelt the sausages burning in the frying pan and ran back to the stove.

"I don't know ..." said Joyce, biting the end of her biro.

The sausages were turned and Mike rushed back to the kitchen table pointing the spatula at the directory.

"Look, if you go phoning strangers because of some dream you had, well, they ... they can lock you up for that you know?"

Joyce took her glasses off and sighed, "Mike, what if I'm right? This man will die from a heart attack in a day or so."

Mike sighed too.

"Even if you were right, say these dreams are some sort of ... what do you call them ...?"

"Premonitions."

"Yeah, premonitions. Even if they are, if he's going to have a heart attack, he's going to have one; what good will it do telling the man he's going to have one?" Mike reasoned, before returning to the crackling sausages.

"Well maybe I can convince him to go and get a check up, or to go to hospital, where they might be able to give him treatment right away if he does have an attack," said Joyce.

"Look, just leave it, love."

Mike tried to lift the sausages on to a plate but dropped one on to the draining board and swore. "Now look what you've made me do. I've ruined the breakfast."

As soon as Mike had gone off to the newsagents to buy cigarettes later that morning, Joyce took a deep breath and telephoned Frank Catergorm. She explained that she was not some nutter, but simply a concerned woman, and she told him about the dream she'd had about Mrs Sugnar and how it had come to pass. She told Frank word for word what the death notice about him had said, and she expected him to hang up, or to swear at her and call her a crackpot – but instead he was intrigued, and was actually a very open-minded man.

"I've been having chest pains," he told Joyce, "and I suppose I've been hiding my head in the sand a bit. You know, trying to convince myself it's indigestion and so on."

"Well, Frank, can you try and get yourself into a hospital tonight?" Joyce asked him, full of concern.

"Tonight?" I'm not a private patient or anything. I can't just phone up Broadgreen Hospital and ask them if they'll have me," was Frank's realistic reply.

"Then you'll just have to pretend," Joyce said, "and I know that's wrong, but you'll have to."

"Pretend?" said Frank with a false laugh.

"Just tell them you've been having chest pains and feel really ill," said Joyce, when she heard the key in the front door. It was Mike returning from the newsagents.

"I could always try. Better to get into trouble with faking symptoms than dying being honest I suppose."

"Frank, I have to go, but before I do, will you please call me back and tell me what happens if you do ... you know ... have an attack?"

Joyce looked up to find Mike standing in the doorway of the living room shaking his head with a look of grave disapproval.

"Ok, erm ... Joyce is it?" Frank asked.

"Yes, Joyce. Good luck and bye for now," she replied and put down the handset.

"After all I said you went and phoned him," said Mike in disgust, then went into the hall to take off his coat.

"Either that or have his death on my conscience," Joyce shouted back.

A few days later, Joyce scanned the obituary pages for a mention of a Frank Catergorm. There was still no mention of his name on the next day or the day after that. She decided to telephone Frank's home, but there was no answer. She therefore called Broadgreen Hospital and queried whether they had a patient by the name of Frank Catergorm. They did. Frank had been admitted earlier in the week and had suffered a cardiac arrest. If it hadn't been for the prompt medical attention he had received, Frank would have died. Joyce learned the full details of this a month later when she visited Frank at his home. He later had heart bypass surgery and is still alive and well today.

After the dream about Frank's death notice, Joyce received no further premonitions in her dreams, and to this day she is at a loss to explain how she came to glimpse information in a newspaper about events in the future.

HAUNTED HOUSE ON DUKE STREET

It all began with faint murmuring sounds at a house on Duke Street in the dead of night in September 2006. At first, twenty-year-old Sarah, a Liverpool John Moore University student, assumed that her flatmate was simply talking in her sleep, but, at precisely four in the morning, she saw exactly where the noise was coming from. Silhouetted against the window was the outline of a woman with her hair tied up in a bun, wearing a puffed-sleeve blouse of some sort. As the student squinted in the half-light, she could also make out a voluminous, bell-shaped dress. The outlandishly dressed stranger was whispering to herself as she looked out of the window.

"Who's that?" Sarah asked, trembling.

She was convinced that it was a ghost from the moment she saw her, not only because of the old-fashioned way in which she was dressed, but also because of the overpowering aura of fear which the apparition gave off.

The shadowy figure turned to face her, and in doing so took on a three dimensional form and made a rustling sound as it approached Sarah's bed. Sarah cringed as the ethereal woman passed straight through the bed and came to a halt in part of the same space which Sarah's legs were occupying. The student felt a loathsome shiver running up her legs, and she ducked under her duvet in revulsion and fear. Eventually the shivering sensation subsided and she plucked up the courage to take a peep from under the duvet. With trepidation, she sneaked a look over the covers, and finding the woman gone from the bed, she surveyed the room. Thankfully, she had vanished.

Sarah sprang out of bed, switched on the light in the flat and violently shook her friend awake. Laura listened intently to what had happened and her face turned ashen and her eyes widened as Sarah described the old fashioned woman. Laura then revealed that she had been having creepy dreams for the past couple of nights in which a Victorian woman – with a high collar and her hair tied up in a bun, just like the one her friend had just described – had been sitting on her bed, stroking her hair as she slept.

In addition to the nocturnal visitor, there were other strange happenings in that bedroom. A chiming clock was heard, even though there was no such clock in the entire house, as well as the distressing sounds of a woman wailing.

Other people in the house on Duke Street also reported having hair-raising encounters with what appears to have been the same outdated woman. A male student returning late to his lodgings on the floor beneath Sarah and Laura was startled to see a Victorian lady fitting the same description standing on the stairs outside his room with a stern and mournful look on her face. The student fumbled with his keys to get into his flat as soon as possible, and listened in dread as the apparition came down the steps towards him. In the nick of time, the student gained entry to his flat and literally slammed the door shut in the woman's face. He was just keying in his brother's number on his mobile, when to his horror, the woman's face came through the door, as if it wasn't there, and peered quizzically at him in the dark hallway. The student was so petrified that he swore and screamed, "Go away!" and the face slowly melted back into the door. The encounter left him feeling extremely jittery and he later moved out of to stay with a friend on Arrad Street.

Not long after his departure, Laura upstairs woke at about 1.30am to go to the toilet. She returned to her bed and tried to fall back to sleep, when she suddenly felt the sensation of someone sitting on the mattress. Then a hand started stroking her hair. At first Laura thought it was Sarah messing about – until she heard her snoring on the other side of the room. She froze and went rigid as the hand continued stroking her hair until finally she let out a scream which awakened her flatmate, and upon which the woman disappeared without a trace.

Enough was enough. The girls confronted the landlord and complained to him about the strange goings-on, and he eventually agreed to give the spooked students new accommodation on the ground floor of the Duke Street house.

After I had heard the girls' story I stayed in the vacated room overnight, and heard footsteps on the stairs when no one was there – well, no one I could see, that is. I also heard a female voice singing what sounded like a lullaby late at night, and something shadowy out of the corner of my eye which flitted about at a phenomenal speed. A medium named Carla was also tried out at this haunted location, and she told me and a fellow researcher that the ghostly woman's name was Louise, and that she was a music teacher who had lived in the house around 1899. Carla believes the surname begins with A, and is possibly Anderson. According to the medium, a teenaged daughter of the woman died of a fever in the room, and 'Louise' thinks one of the students bears a strong likeness to this dead daughter.

After a little research at the library I traced a Louise Anderson, who had indeed been a music teacher in Duke Street in 1900, but at an address which is different from that where the ghostly activity is going on. Carla also claimed that a man with the surname 'Fazakerley' was haunting the house as well, and from what she could discover, he seemed to be trying to encourage Louise to go back to the world of spirit.

Like many cases of this kind, the ghostly goings-on ceased abruptly after a few weeks, and they may never return again.

PHANTASMS OF FEAR

Ghosts, by their very nature, usually startle and scare people, because they behave in ways that we are not accustomed to, and they often seem to contravene the everyday laws of physics by floating about above the ground and vanishing into thin air, or walking through solid walls.

Amongst the ghostly population of Merseyside, there are apparitions and manifestations that are particularly creepy and instill fear in all though who witness them. Here are just a few of these eerie ectoplasmic phantasms.

***

One dusky evening in 1991, fifteen-year-old Leah Jones was idly gazing out of the back bedroom window of her house on Moscow Drive in the Stoneycroft area of Liverpool, daydreaming about a boy she had fallen in love with, when something caught her attention out of the corner of her eye. She leaned out of the open window to get a better look at whatever it was that she had seen. A shadowy shape, resembling a man lying face down on the top of the backyard wall, was moving along in a very peculiar and frightening way. He was somehow dragging himself along the top of the wall by clawing his way with his bare hands. He continued to slither along the top of the wall on his stomach, and as Leah followed his progress with a trembling hand to her mouth, the dark-clad figure suddenly slid off the wall and down into the alleyway, as if he had been stuck to the bricks, like a gecko.

Leah ran out of her bedroom and downstairs to the kitchen, where her mother was busy washing the dishes. She gave an excited and slightly garbled account of the strange crawling man, and Leah's mother tutted and said she must have been seeing things. Her mother's reaction infuriated Leah and she repeated her story, this time even more vehemently, so that Mrs Jones was forced to accept that something had really upset her daughter, but since there was no longer any sign of anything in the backyard, there was nothing she could do about it..

On the following evening at 7pm, Leah was in her bedroom once more, and this time she was with her school-friend Rachael, who was perched on the edge of the bed, gently strumming an acoustic guitar, when the two girls heard a dog in a neighbour's yard let out a blood-curdling howl. They looked at each other then rushed to the window, which they lifted open. They popped their heads out of the window and looked over into next door's backyard. The old Labrador was sitting upright in the centre of the yard, alternating between howling and growling at something on the wall. As the girls' eyes adjusted to the darkness, they could slowly make out something long and dark creeping along the top of the wall like a snake. Leah gasped in shock, because she instantly recognised the slinking man.

"What on earth is it?" Rachael asked. The thing frightened her, although she couldn't make out exactly what it was.

The man was dressed in dark clothes and was facing downwards, but his hands could be clearly seen because of their contrasting pasty colour. The girls watched, mesmerised, as the ghostly hands clawed at the gaps between the bricks on top of the wall as the serpent-like figure dragged itself effortlessly along. The legs didn't seem to move at all and the body was also totally inert. Only the arms and hands moved. The face didn't turned upwards, so the girls never saw what this freakish man looked like.

Leah walked towards the bedroom door, intending to shout down the stairs to her mum and dad and brother, but Rachael cried, "No. Please don't leave me!"

Leah therefore returned to the window, and she and her friend watched the creepy man, or whatever it was, as he progressed slowly along like a snail or a slug along the backyard wall, until he was lost in the gloom.

That same night, Leah's mother heard all about the slithery man from a different source. Her neighbour Mrs Wright called round to tell her about the thing that had been seen crawling along the backyard walls of Moscow Drive and to ask if she had noticed anything unusual. At first, when Mrs Wright had spotted the man she had assumed that it was a burglar climbing into her yard as she watched his progress from her bedroom window, but she was unnerved by the way he sloped along in a way that no normal person could. He seemed to have no backbone, or was double-jointed, because, on reaching the wall of an end house, he climbed it vertically like an insect, and at one point his legs and lower abdomen were still flat against the top of the wall, but his upper body and arms were flush against the vertical wall, so that his body was bent at a ninety degree angle. The weird-looking figure then clambered away into the darkness and seemed to vanish altogether.

There were other sightings of the slithering apparition crawling along the backyard walls of Moscow Drive and they lasted for about a week, then they became less frequent as the summer nights gradually arrived; but who knows? Perhaps the crawling man will make a comeback one day.

***

One of the oddest types of ghost in the world of the supernatural is the entity that gets about; an apparition that haunts places which are miles apart, sometimes simultaneously, sometimes years apart. In the following case, perhaps two identical, or similar-looking ghosts, were at work in the mid-1980s.

Bebington Cemetery over in Wirral is located at the junction of Town and Townfield Lanes, near to the Oval Sports Centre. Among the many people lying at rest in there, are several of the men who perished in the *Thetis* submarine tragedy in 1939. Every stone in the cemetery tells a story, and some of them are very strange.

There is one grave that contains the body of a Birkenhead woman who passed away in the early 1960s. The woman was elderly and her health had been deteriorating for some time. She finally died at her home near Exmouth Street, but her son was so distressed at losing his beloved mother, that he attempted to bring her back to life by digging down to her coffin and 'rescuing' her from the fate of decay in the realm of worms. In the mind of this man, who was unhinged by his grief, he believed that instead of waiting for the mass resurrection of Judgement Day, he could revive his mother there and then and he had a carefully thought out plan of action.

He decided that he would first infuse some chemical-based energy into the lifeless body by stuffing its mouth with glucose sweets. He then resorted to wiring his mother up to the mains electricity supply in an effort to resurrect her. Perhaps the muscles of the corpse twitched and spasms rippled through the decrepit limbs, but, unsurprisingly, the spark of life could not be rekindled. Sometimes it is almost impossible to let a loved person leave our life, but when death takes them, there is little we can do except hope they are at peace, and if we have sufficient faith, we may look forward to joining them in the hereafter one day.

The Frankenstein-like son was watched by curious neighbours entering and leaving a certain house that served as his ad hoc laboratory, and in the end the authorities swooped on this grim premises and came upon the exhumed corpse, lying on its unfurled burial shroud with sweets swelling its bulging cheeks, making the head look like some gruesome hamster. Wires trailed from the decaying body to the mains electricity outlets. The police initially thought they had uncovered the lair of some kind of necrophiliac pervert, but soon realised that the poor man was simply deranged with grief. Their disgust turned to sympathy towards him, and no charges were brought against him. The old woman was solemnly re-interred in Bebington Cemetery, where she silently awaits that promised day when the dead shall rise again from their graves.

***

At Bebington Cemetery in the summer of 1985, Mohammed and Ryan, two thirteen-year-old boys, had decided to go and take a look around the graves and the chapel of rest, simply out of mischievous curiosity, but they soon regretted entering the place of the dead on that sunny afternoon. Mohammed was the first to notice the 'thing' peeping over the top of a headstone about forty feet away. It looked like the shiny bald pate of a man crouching behind the stone, only it was as pale as milk.

"What is that?" Ryan asked, squinting into the sunlight at the domed head peeping now from the side of the gravestone.

"Somebody messing about," Mohammed decided, but nevertheless he backed away from the eerie peeking head, because they could see no eyes in what they assumed to be someone's head.

The white domed head disappeared behind the gravestone only to reappear partially behind another one about twenty feet away, where it began to protrude over the top of the stone, as if it was watching the boys, or perhaps playing some sort of game.

Children are often good judges of what is benign or evil in the world of the supernatural, and Mohammed and Ryan instinctively turned away from the pale skull-like head and bolted out of the cemetery as though they had spied the Devil himself. Once outside the cemetery walls they both agreed that the thing peering over the gravestones was something very sinister indeed.

A year afterwards, the same peeping ghost was seen once again, this time stealing sly glances at children who were watching it from a nearby playground. The children had climbed on top of the monkey bars of the playground, and from that vantage point they were able to look over the high walls of the cemetery into the burial ground, and they shuddered as they saw the dome-headed ghost flitting about the place; popping up between the branches of trees to look at them, and darting behind one gravestone after another. The children became so scared by the antics of the ghost, that they climbed down off the monkey bars and ran back home in panic.

Around the same time, a similar pale, featureless ghost was also peeping at people in Allerton Cemetery in Liverpool. On this occasion, the coy apparition was not seen by children, but by a retired doctor and two elderly ladies who were on their way to the cemetery to lay flowers on the grave of a friend. Mrs Marsha Huntley was the first person to see the snow-white, balloon-like head bobbing up and down from behind a tall black marble gravestone about fifty yards away from the Springwood Avenue entrance to the cemetery. Marsha immediately drew her friends' attention to the bobbing white object. As all three looked on in bewilderment, the white spot in the distance peeped over a grave and then moved at a phenomenal speed between the rows of headstones. At one point the women yelped with fear as the baffling white globular head briefly emerged from behind a headstone less than ten feet away from them, before ducking back behind the gravestone markers.

***

At a certain house in the Georgian Quarter of Liverpool city centre, a particularly sadistic ghost is, by all accounts, still active, some eighty years after it was first encountered.

Around 1926, a large family by the name of Hart moved into the Georgian terraced house, and during the first night at their new home, something terrifying took place in the bedroom of the Hart's thirteen-year-old daughter. The girl's harrowing screams echoed throughout the house at just after eleven o'clock, and her two sisters and three brothers, accompanied by their father, burst into her bedroom. She was lying on the bed sobbing and clutching her left arm. Apparently, she she had been awakened by a tall man who had been leaning over her bed. She was unable to get a description of his face in the dark, but she could make out his white starched cuffs as he pinned her down and inserted a long-needled brass syringe into her forearm. When his daughter's arm was inspected by gaslight, Mr Hart could clearly see a distinct crimson spot left by the needle.

Every nook and cranny in the attic was searched, just in case some maniac was hiding up there ready to attack again, but they found no one. Furthermore, the attic was heavily draped in cobwebs and looked as if no one had been up there in decades.

Despite taking every precaution to protect his family, Mr Hart's two other daughters allegedly felt the ghost's needle on two further occasions and on the second of these one of the victims caught sight of a man in a long black coat appearing in her bedroom one night when the full moon was shining through her bedroom window. The girl watched, petrified, as the man produced a long brass syringe from what looked like a Gladstone bag before he confronted her. She screamed and hid under the blankets, but she felt a large, cold, powerful hand seize her hand and unfurl her clenched fingers. Next came a sharp, agonising pain as the needle pierced her palm and came out on the other side of her hand. She looked up, paralysed with fear, and saw a man of about forty with short dark hair parted in the centre, and a pair of demonic dark eyes. He said something which the girl couldn't understand as he withdrew the needle from her hand. He then turned and went back towards his Gladstone bag, at which point the girl suddenly regained the power of movement, and she bolted from the bed and out of the bedroom screaming. On this occasion, no evidence of any needle wound was detectable, but when her father and brothers entered the room they could all smell the strong aroma of ether hanging in the air.

The ghost of what was assumed to be a doctor or surgeon remained at large in the upper rooms of the house for many months, and during that time the needle was felt by all the female members of the household, including the mother, but the males were never touched.

One night, Mrs Hart was awakened in her bed by an agonising pain in her big toe. At the bottom of the bed she could see the faint outline of a man crouching between the bedposts. She instinctively kicked out at him and her bare foot, instead of making contact with his head, went straight through the ashen oval that was his face. It was like kicking thin air. Mr Hart was shaken awake by his hysterical wife, and he lit the gas mantle before inspecting the bottom of the bed, but as on all previous occasions, there was no sign of the cruel needle-toting spectre.

The family reluctantly moved from the residence, and further reports of the sadistic doctor's activities are hard to find – until the twenty-first century. The house in question was recently divided into luxury apartments, and in 2005, a young professional woman in her twenties named Molly moved into one of them. About a week after moving in, Molly was sitting up in bed one night, reading a book, when she heard a distinct short cough in the bedroom. She looked about her, and because she was troubled by the sound, she tried to rationalise what she had heard by thinking the window must be open and that the sound had come from outside in the street – but when she looked up, she found that the window was firmly closed.

About an hour later, Molly had forgotten about the strange cough, and had started to feel drowsy as she finished the chapter of her book. She turned off the bedside lamp, and soon fell into a deep, satisfying sleep. She had a nightmare about being stung by a huge, grotesque-looking wasp, and the dream was so realistic, that she could feel a searing pain in the back of her hand. She awoke, startled, to find a man kneeling at her bedside. He had his hand under the blanket and was softly stroking her thigh, but his hand felt stone cold. Molly's right hand was hurting badly, but nevertheless she was ready to strike the man's face with it, when suddenly, a strange numbness seeped over her body. She tried to lift her arm to push the silhouetted stranger away, but her arm felt as if it was a dead weight. The man then stopped rubbing her leg and assaulted her, and she was powerless to stop him. She tried to cry out, but her tongue felt swollen and numb too, as if she had been injected with cocaine.

After he had finished his violation of her, he got to his feet, and moved towards the window. The faint light filtering in through the blinds illuminated Molly's attacker and clearly showed what he was wearing: a white starched collar, a waistcoat, a long-sleeved shirt and a pair of black trousers. The man had a clean-shaven pale face with dark staring eyes, and short black hair parted in the centre. He leaned over Molly once more and then pulled away the duvet. He started to fondle her breasts through her tee shirt, but she felt so outraged by the assault, that, despite her parched mouth, she somehow managed to force out a scream, to which the intruder seemed to recoil. The feeling had started to return to her limbs and she sat up and slapped him across the face, and something horrific took place. Molly's hand disarranged his features as if they were moulded from putty. The impact of her hand sent the nose and lips sideways, leaving the face totally disfigured. To Molly's hand, his face felt as if it was made out of something earthy and clay-like.

The figure turned and ran straight through a dresser and vanished into the wall. Molly started to hyperventilate with the shock, and she stumbled out of the bed, switched on the light, and looked at the place where the ghost had seemingly disappeared into the solid wall. The numbness continued to fade away, and as it did so, Molly became aware of the stabbing pain in her right hand again. When she looked at the centre of her palm, she saw a tiny hole. Was this from the needle of the misogynistic ghost?

Molly soon discovered that the ghost seemed to be repelled by light, for on the second encounter with the spook, she saw it emerging from the wardrobe mirror one morning as she got up to go to the bathroom. As soon as she switched on the light, the phantom grimaced and fled back to wherever it had come from. Since Molly started sleeping with a nightlight permanently on and a Bible by her bedside, the ghost has not returned to bother her.

I have researched the history of the house and discovered that there was a doctor who had his surgery at the dwelling in Edwardian times, but whether it is his revenant that haunts that address today is difficult to say. If I were to start investigating him with the help of a medium, it could make matters worse and end up irritating him and provoking further attacks. Better to let sleeping ghosts lie, I always say.

REFLECTIONS OF THE FUTURE

One Sunday in 1957, six-year-old Cathy was taken by her mother to visit her grandmother at Walton Park Gardens, on Queen's Drive. Little Cathy wore a beautiful white dress, reserved for these weekend visits, and as her mother chatted to her Gran, the girl wandered out of the living room and into the spare bedroom, where she did a twirl and took a look at herself dressed in her Sunday best in the mirror of an old wardrobe. What happened next would haunt the child well into adulthood.

The figure of a woman slid into view in the wardrobe mirror, and she resembled Cathy's mother, except that her hairstyle and clothes were different. The girl turned around, confused, thinking she was seeing her mother's reflection, but no one else was in the room. The woman in the mirror smiled down at Cathy, and the child ran out of the bedroom and straight into the living room, where she threw herself on to her mother's lap. Cathy looked back at the door as if she expected the woman in the wardrobe mirror to follow her into the living room, and then she told her mother what she had seen.

"She's got a vivid imagination," her Gran said, but Cathy's mum could see that something had terrified her child and seriously wondered whether she had seen a ghost.

Six years later, the grandmother passed away, and Cathy's mother came into possession of the old wardrobe. By now, Cathy was twelve, and yet she could still vividly recall the smiling woman in that wardrobe mirror. At this time, the family were living in a four-bedroomed house in Ellesmere Port, and the spooky old wardrobe had been put in Cathy's brother Michael's room.

One Saturday afternoon when Michael was out playing football, Cathy went rooting about in his room to see if she could find some money for sweets, and as she was looking under his mattress, she had the eerie feeling that she was being watched. Then she caught a fleeting movement in the corner of her eye. She turned towards the wardrobe and there was the same woman she had seen six years before, staring at her from the wardrobe's looking glass. She wore a maroon polo-neck top, and a silver pendant, and she smiled at Cathy, but the smile did nothing to ally her fears and she fled from the room and down the stairs three at a time to tell her father what she had seen. He offered the usual explanations which adults propound when they are unable to rationalise something outside of their experience.

"Hey! Calm down, Cathy," her father said, without looking up from his newspaper. "You've seen your mum's reflection, that's all."

"But mum's at the shops," Cathy reminded him. "So how could I?" but her father turned the page and just nodded. He wasn't even listening.

Cathy saw that same woman in the mirror of the wardrobe on three more occasions in that year.

In 1977, Cathy was twenty-six years of age with a three-year-old child, and by then was living in Halton, Runcorn. As she had very little furniture, her mother had given her the 'haunted' wardrobe when she moved into her new house, and Cathy installed the antique in her own bedroom. One day she was looking at herself in the mirror of that wardrobe, when she suddenly recognised the ghostly woman she had seen all those years ago.

It was herself – her own reflection.

Cathy now wore the very same hairstyle, the same maroon polo-neck sweater, and a silver pendant. She was stunned by this sudden realisation. Somehow, twenty years ago, her younger self had seen her twenty-six-year-old self in 1977, but just how that had been possible is an enigma which will puzzle Cathy to her dying day.

ROY THE RING

One balmy evening in the summer of 1979, the sun was setting between the towers of the Liver Buildings, and its short-lived blood-orange glare bathed the windows of the four-storey, yellow-brick homes on Gambier Terrace, situated on the brow of St James's Mount.

Along the private carriageway running parallel to the row of terraced houses, a chain of teenaged girls linking one another's arms and strolled along, singing the Peaches and Herb song, 'Reunited'. A green analogue telephone, the type with the rotating dial that we see no more, started to ring at a flat on the second floor of one of the houses on Gambier Terrace, and fifty-nine-year-old Betty answered it.

"Hello?" she said twice, but heard nothing. Then came a dead tone. Betty took a look at the clock on the mantelpiece which gave the time as 8.40pm. "That's strange," she muttered to herself, then shrugged, and to her vanilla-coloured cat, Mr Tibbs, she said: "Perhaps it was a wrong number."

She sat down to watch her black and white television, looking forward to seeing *New At Ten*, as she was a woman who liked to know what was going on in the world. The window and the television were her portals to the world outside, being a person who suffered from agoraphobia; a fear of going outside to mingle amongst people. The phobia had first manifested itself a few years back, after the death of Betty's husband. It just came out of the blue after the panic attacks started. She had been in the flat at Gambier Terrace for two years now and she felt more comfortable tucked away off Hope Street. She was a recluse who had no inclination to mingle amongst the crowds of the city centre.

The green telephone rang again, and Betty gripped the arms of her wing chair and levered herself up with a groan of annoyance. Once again she picked up the receiver and said, "Hello?" but this time a low menacing voice asked, "Did you know your flat is haunted?"

"I beg your pardon? Could you speak up?" Betty replied, and she leaned forward towards the television and turned down the volume.

"Your flat is haunted," said the unknown caller, "and everyone who lives in that flat ends up dead."

The caller then hung up, leaving Betty on the verge of a panic attack. She gazed out at the dominating hulk of the Gothic cathedral, silhouetted now against a strange malachite-green sky that faded into Prussian blue. If that message had come through in the daytime she would have dismissed it as a nuisance call, but now, with twilight closing in, Betty imagined the call as something far more sinister. She drew the curtains and then sat perched on the edge of her chair, looking at the telephone and trying to suppress that all too familiar feeling of rising panic.

Just then the door of the kitchen creaked open and Betty gulped with fear. But it was only Mr Tibbs, pawing the door open for her to get to his supper before he was let out. Betty went to the kitchen to watch her only loyal friend eat his food in his usual delicate way, and she dreaded the thought of going to let him out. What if the creepy caller was lying in wait downstairs?

She watched the rest of *News At Ten*, and after the programme had finished, gave herself a stern talking to and decided to risk taking Tibbs downstairs. After all, it was probably just some prankster who had called her earlier, having chosen her number at random, she reasoned.

Tibbs was let out at 11pm. He looked back at Betty, then silently padded off into his nocturnal world. Betty closed the front door and hurried back to her flat upstairs. She bolted the door that night – just to be on the safe side.

At four in the morning, the telephone rang. Betty flung back the covers and walked into the living room, but she started to shake. Her stomach turned over with every ring of the telephone, and she wondered whether she should put some pillows over the thing. But eventually she answered it, and once more there was silence at the other end of the line. She was about to put the receiver down when a voice suddenly said: "Betty, there are ghosts and evil things in your flat, and they will kill you if you don't leave."

Then the caller hung up.

Right there and then, Betty went to her sideboard, opened a drawer, and rummaged about for a piece of pink paper. She dialled the number upon it and roused her niece Patricia, who had been sleeping soundly in bed at her Tuebrook home. Patricia promised she would call in to see Betty around 9am, and she advised her to leave the telephone off the hook until then.

"It's probably someone just messing about Betty," Patricia said, trying to reassure her aunt. "You get to bed and take no notice of these loonies. I'll see you in the morning."

Betty took her niece's advice after apologising to her for waking her at such an unearthly hour. So, the phone was left off the hook as directed, and Betty went to bed, but she barely slept a wink all night.

Some days later, the telephone rang in the middle of the afternoon and the familiar menacing voice rasped, "The angel of death will descend on you soon, Betty. Leave your home while you still have a chance," and then the line went dead.

Betty summoned all her willpower and paid a visit to the police station on Hope Street, where she was told to keep a log of the calls; what time the man was calling and exactly what he said. In the meantime, the police would liaise with the telephone company to try and ascertain where the anonymous caller was phoning from. This, of course, was back in the days when 1471 was unheard of, so you couldn't discover the caller's telephone number from your home telephone set. The telephone company discovered that the caller had telephoned twice from a call box at the bottom of Mount Pleasant, near the Shaftsbury Hotel. Another call had been made a stone's throw away, on the corner of Oxford Street, facing the Metropolitan Cathedral. When Betty's niece Patricia would telephone, she and her aunt could often hear clicks on the line as the police listened in, hoping to catch the threatening caller.

One evening the faceless caller rang, and once again he began to frighten Betty with threats of impending doom from the spirits in her flat, when there was a loud audible click on the line. Suspecting the phone line was being tapped, he slammed down the receiver. This call, it transpired after painstaking checks at the local telephone exchanges, had been made at a telephone box on Rodney Street.

After that, the sinister calls stopped for almost a fortnight, and something else reared its head to worry Betty. Her cat, Mr Tibbs, went missing. Three days later, an envelope containing a disturbing letter was posted to Betty's home. The author of the missive claimed that he had the cat, and unless Betty left her haunted home, he'd kill the feline and post its head to her. The writer assured Betty that he had no qualms about beheading a cat, as he was a practising Satanist, and the note was signed with a drawing of a pentagram.

Betty suffered a collapse after reading that evil letter and later that day she was taken to hospital and treated for shock. Her nephew Carl visited her at the hospital, and promised his aunt that he'd get to the bottom of the matter. Carl worked at the Ford car plant at Halewood, yet he had always harboured a secret ambition to become a private detective for years. He interviewed his aunt's neighbours in Gambier Terrace and made enquiries about who had lived in her flat before her, two years previously. Only a few residents could remember who this person was. He was a man in his twenties called Roy, and he had lived alone. That was all they could tell him, and it certainly didn't give him much to go on. Carl asked his aunt if she had ever received any junk mail addressed to a Roy at her flat, and Betty suddenly remembered that she had. The letters had been final demands from a book club and had been addressed to a Roy Kelley, demanding payment for books he had requested. With this name in mind, Carl sat down and thought about the places where the caller had telephoned from – Mount Pleasant, Oxford Street and Rodney Street. His intuition told him that this Roy fellow might have something to do with a place in that area where young men would congregate and even live – the Young Man's Christian Association – the YMCA on Mount Pleasant. It was a long shot, but Carl went along there and sat in the lounge, drinking a coffee as he cogitated on the problem at hand. He finally approached the kitchen staff at the canteen and casually asked, "Is Roy Kelley about?"

"Roy Kelley? What does he look like?" asked the girl behind the counter.

"Er... he's about that big, er ... Carl struggled to provide a description of a man he'd never set eyes on before.

"You mean Roy the Ring?" a female cook said, emerging from the back-kitchen.

"Is his name Kelley?" the girl in blue overall asked her colleague.

The cook looked at Carl and smiled, as Carl was quite a handsome man who looked a lot younger than his forty years.

"Yeah," said the cook. "He's Barry Kelley's cousin."

"Yes, that's him," said Carl, trying to sound confident and he ordered a sandwich.

"Are you his mate?" the cook asked.

"Yeah ... erm ... I used to work with him," Carl stammered. He was such an terrible liar, he was sure they would see straight through him.

"You mean Roy the Ring actually *worked*?" the cook asked, with a bemused grin.

She got into conversation with Carl, and after introducing herself as Claudia, she gave the amateur private enquiry agent a potted history of Roy's criminal career. He had stolen two hundred zircon rings from a factory a few years previously and had stashed them away before he was sent down for another less serious crime. He had boasted to anyone who cared to listen that he had hidden the rings in a flat before he was arrested and sentenced, but after getting out of the nick a few months back he had discovered that "some old biddy" was living in the flat where the rings were stashed. Barely able to breathe with excitement, Carl asked Claudia where this flat was.

"Oh, as if he's going to tell me that! Act your age,!" was her reply.

Carl was convinced that those rings were stashed somewhere in Aunt Betty's flat, so, having gained what he was looking for, he made an excuse to leave, and told Claudia he'd soon be back.

Carl searched every inch of the flat at Gambier Terrace. He tapped the floorboards, the walls, and he even checked the enamel tiles in the bathroom, just in case one was loose. In the kitchen, his eyes wandered up to the ventilator grille; was it possible that the rings could be stored in there? He found a torch, climbed up on to a kitchen unit and shone a light through the grille, but the ventilator's interior was completely clear, and he could see daylight filtering through.

Carl trawled through the house again with a fine toothed comb, but without success, then went to the toilet. Whilst sitting on the toilet seat he noticed that the panel on the side of the bath seemed to have come loose. He prised it off – and behind it, wrapped up in plastic carrier bags, he found one hundred and ninety seven small red boxes, each containing a zircon ring. Carl went straight to the police, and they descended upon Roy Kelley at the YMCA. He eventually confessed to making the threatening calls to Betty, in the hope that he would get her to leave his former flat. Roy knew the vulnerable woman's telephone number because that number had once been his. He had discovered Betty's name by simply phoning her one day and asking her if her gas supply was on, because he was an engineer from North West Gas in the street outside, working on the pipes. During the conversation he asked Betty if she could confirm her name, and she had foolishly given it to him in good faith. He and a friend known as Irish Joe had even planned to break into the house to retrieve the zircon rings, but the old woman hardly ever went out.

The kidnapped cat Mr Tibbs was found at Irish Joe's flat on Roscoe Street completely unharmed; Betty made a full recovery, and returned to her reclusive life at the flat on Gambier Terrace; and her nephew, to whom she would be eternally grateful, later moved to London, where he ended up running his own detective agency.

THE SPEAKING CAT OF SPEKE

From its days as the adjoining hamlet of Oglet, nestled in the lee of the Mersey, to its status today as a prominent town within its own right, Speke has undergone many changes. In the early 1950s, Western Avenue was a long and lonely lane with a pot-holed surface, bordered by grasslands on one side, and the 'Little Woods' on the other, and it was within this secluded woodland that something very strange took place in early November 1953.

It was during the days leading up to Guy Fawkes Night, that magical time for children between Halloween and Yuletide. Twelve-year-old David from a prefab on Rycot Road, and Alan, his eleven-year-old friend from Hale Road, decided to play cowboys and Indians in the Little Woods. These days such an escapade, without adult supervision, would be unheard of, but the fifties was a time before children were routinely wrapped in cottonwool for the whole of their childhood.

The time was 4.20pm. An autumn mist was drifting in from the direction of the distant airport runways, and darkness was falling fast, so the two boys built a small fire in the woods. Alan's prized possessions were his bow and arrows, and he dipped the head of one of the wooden arrows into the fire, and when it was well alight, he fired it into the air. It climbed like a rocket into the darkening sky and arced over the crowns of the bare-branched trees into the murky depths of the misty wood. Alan expected David to make some complimentary remark about his archery skills, but his friend was too busy looking at something else in the wood, with a transfixed expression somewhere between fear and wonder.

Alan turned to see what had captured David's attention, and was startled to see a strange-looking animal about twenty feet away. The light of the flickering fire illuminated the form of an enormous, tabby-coloured cat, about four feet in height, and it sat there with a peculiar expression on its face. Its blue eyes were almost human-looking and full of wisdom.

"Hello, children," the feline said in a clear, rather well-spoken voice.

The boys reacted to the speaking cat by fleeing from the woods on to Western Avenue, where they narrowly missed being hit by the 82E bus. The bus driver beeped his horn and shook his fist at the children before continuing on his way. Minutes later, the boys reached Alan's home on Hale Road and blabbed out their incredible story, but no one believed them. Let's face it, a four-foot-tall cat was unbelievable enough, but a cat that spoke?

The boys plucked up all their courage and returned to the wood on the following day at around the same time, and again built a fire. Sure enough, the oversized striped cat came slinking silently out of the wood towards David and Alan, who were, as you might expect, pretty nervous. The cat arched its great back, then snuggled down by the fire, and from the other side of the flames, the boys watched tensely. Before long the cat started to speak. It gave its name as something that sounded like Semeel, and claimed to be a guardian. Semeel warned the children to stay away from the wood, claiming that a certain man whom they both knew was out to kill them. After this startling pronouncement the cat vanished back into the wood.

The lads returned to their homes and told their parents what the giant cat had told them, and both were scolded for telling silly lies. What's more, the man who was supposedly out to kill them was on holiday in Wales at the time. However, a week later, this man was found, dressed as a vagrant, hiding out in the woods. He had built a den there after secretly returning from Wales. The matter was reported to the police who discovered that the same man had attempted to abduct a child five years before in Widnes, and he then confessed that it had been his intention to abduct David and Alan.

Semeel was seen by the boys on three more occasions, but when the area was cleared for building developments, the enigmatic speaking cat of Speke was seen no more.

SEASON OF THE WITCH

When I was a child on Halloween, my grandmother would recite this old rhyme:

When the world is wrapped in slumber
And the moon is sailing high,
If you peep between the curtains
You'll see witches riding by

And I would dare myself to peep between the curtains, always hoping I'd see a witch flying by on her broomstick. My older, teenaged sister was a practising witch at the time, and whenever she was out, I'd flip through her books of spells, and look at her talismans, mortar and pestle, crystals, wax effigies and other Wiccan paraphernalia. My sister would usually scare me when she came home, because she uncannily seemed to know exactly what I had touched in her room. She'd promise to curse me with all kinds of nasty hexes because I'd been prying about in her 'sanctum', as she called it.

Being of Celtic descent, I have always sensed some great but subtle change literally hanging in the air during the season of the witch – Halloween. Even as a child I knew that there was some ancient occult subtext to 'Duck-Apple Night', when my mother would tie cotton threads to the stalks of apples and suspend them on doorframes. She would also put apples with coins pushed into them in a bowl of water, and I would have to kneel at the bowl and seize the apple with my mouth to claim it. I later learned that the apple was the Celtic fruit of the Otherworld which had magical properties, and that the Isle of Apples was known as Avalon to the ancient Celts. I also discovered that the apples had long been regarded as a symbol of youth, and that in Scandinavian mythology, the gods tasted the Golden Apples whenever they wished to renew their youth.

I would often watch my Wiccan sisters standing before a mirror after midnight at Halloween, combing their long hair as they bit into apples. They both reported seeing men's faces in the mirror appearing over their shoulders as they did this – an ancient way of discovering what your future husband or wife would look like. They both saw the faces of the men they would one day marry.

My mother read cards – not those of the Tarot – but everyday playing cards, and she always seemed uncannily close, or spot-on in her interpretation of the dealt hand. My grandmother read tea-leaves, and her female friend was an accurate psychic who could tell when a person was going to die by the state of their aura. It soon became clear to me that all women seemed to be born witches or had the potential to become witches. 'Female intuition' was a term males used for the sixth sense women had, but I came to know better: the pineal gland in the female – long associated with the legendary Third Eye – is larger than the male one.

When I was fourteen I sat down in front of the glowing orange coals of a fire with my grandmother one autumn evening as she peeled potatoes, and I gazed into the tiny blue 'fairy flames' and asked her if there were such things as real witches on broomsticks. Here is the tale she told me.

In 1786, Castle Street was widened to allow more traffic and pedestrians better access to the burgeoning thoroughfares of Dale Street and Lord Street. Before the widening of Castle Street, two carriages could barely squeeze past one another in its narrow lanes. Many old crumbling houses were pulled down during the redevelopment, and new private properties were erected in their place. An old tenant named Mary Gore was forced to move out of her ancient wooden home on Castle Street, and the paltry compensation money she was given by the Liverpool Corporation was stolen from her by the foreman of a group of builders who were erecting Heywoods Bank. Mary Gore cursed the foreman, and was forced to go and stay with her sister Isabel, who worked at the Golden Lion Inn on Dale Street. The foreman, whose name was John Collins, was told by one of the Irish workmen that Mary Gore was a witch, and that her coven was to be avoided at all costs. The Irishman advised his boss to give back the money he had stolen from Mary, or face the lethal might of the coven's magic.

Collins ordered the Irishman to get on with his work, and ridiculed the old woman and the idea of her being a witch, but, despite the foreman's scepticism, Mary Gore was indeed a witch, and belonged to a coven that was feared right across England. Most of the witches of the coven lived at an old house situated in a dark alleyway off Dale Street. When Mr Collins went to the Golden Lion Inn on Dale Street during the afternoon break, he heard more about these witches from an old sea captain with whom he got into conversation. The captain, a Mr Harrison, said that the witches had a great black metal cauldron which they used to boil up unholy concoctions consisting of the parts of corpses stolen from local churchyards. The witches had also been seen flying out of the garret window of the house on broomsticks, and sailors and captains had even seen them soaring high above the masts of their ships at sea. The witches regularly flew to Wales, the Isle of Man, and some even ranged as far as Ireland on their mysterious journeys.

"What absolute nonsense," scoffed Collins, but nevertheless he seemed decidedly nervous.

Mary Gore came up to the foreman in the tavern and pointed him out to her sister Isabel, saying, "This is the blaggard who stole my money from me. I have cursed him to die a slow and painful death."

Mr Collins hurled his flagon of ale at the old crone, which caused her to fly at him and try to claw at his face, but her sister pulled her back and shepherded her upstairs to her room in the tavern.

Later that day, the builders left the site on Castle Street and were starting to travel back to their homes, when a dense fog came creeping up James Street from the Mersey. It blotted out virtually everything, and within minutes, the foreman was stumbling over the mounds of rubble at the Castle Street demolition site, as he tried to make his way home. Then people in the area heard a man shouting, followed by awful screams – and these sounds seemed to come from above.

When the fog cleared on the following morning, no one could find Mr Collins anywhere. Then one of the workers noticed something very out of the ordinary. There was something caught on the weather vane of the Exchange building in the distance. Those with good eyesight said it looked like a man, and when they got nearer to the building, they confirmed that it was indeed a man, impaled through his mid-section on the weather vane. A sea captain unfolded his telescope and studied the grisly sight, and reported that it was a red-headed man. His blood had trickled down the weather vane and dripped upon the domed roof of the Exchange.

A crowd began to gather, and people wondered who the man could be. A balloonist by the name of Lunardi had recently flown over the area, and some wondered if the impaled man had perhaps fallen out of the balloon, but one of the people who looked through the captain's telescope at the man who had been spitted on the weather vane immediately recognised him as Mr Collins, the foreman of the Castle Street builders, but how on earth had he ended up skewered on the weather vane hundreds of feet up in the air?

As the crowd watched, a number of large black birds flew from the north and circled the roof of the Exchange. It was a muster of crows, and they flew at the impaled corpse and started pecking at it. To the carrion crows Collins's body was nothing more than their next meal. As the authorities made plans to retrieve the body, the crows continued to tear at its flesh until it was reduced to a red glistening mess.

At one o'clock in the afternoon, a violent thunderstorm struck the town, and as stinging hailstones pelted down on the morbid sightseers who had gathered to gawp at the impaled man, a powerful bolt of lightning hit the weathervane. The body was partly scorched by the lightning and it fell apart and dropped to the street below. The legs, torso, arms, intestines, and head bounced off the domed roof and fell on to the crowd who shrieked in disgust. The extensive bloodstain on the dome remained for several weeks, until the rains washed it away, and the various parts of Mr Collins' body were buried in a pauper's grave at a local churchyard.

The workers continued building the bank on Castle Street, but each day during their lunch break, they would speculate upon how their late foreman had ended up run through by a weather vane. A slow-witted lad named Samuel, who helped out on the building site, claimed that he had seen what had happened to Mr Collins that day. The boy struggled to find adequate words to describe what he remembered in his mind, but finally he managed to spit out this gem to his engrossed listeners: "The women came down and they took him up into the air."

"What women, Sam?" asked one of the builders, eager to know more.

"Women, all in black, sitting on brooms, they took him up," Samuel replied, and started to grin as he recalled how the witches had swooped down on Mr Collins and grabbed him. Then they had impaled him on the cast iron weather vane, their punishment for stealing from a member of their coven named Mary Gore.

The builders found it hard to believe Samuel's incredible story, yet they knew the boy never lied; he wasn't capable.

When my Grandmother had related that hoary old tale, she told me with a half-smile that the witches of Mary Gore's coven had descendants all over Merseyside, and the tiny blue flames of the fire sputtered.

THE KNOWSLEY DEMON

In the summer of 1967, Chris and Gerry, two struggling actors in their twenties, were becoming quite determined to forge their way into that hive of thespian talent at Number 9 Hope Street – the Everyman Theatre Limited. The two young men sat at a table in the window of the El Cabala coffee bar on Bold Street, talking.

"Have you ever seen the fourth wall?" Gerry asked earnestly, mulling over his spiralling stirred coffee, his hands pressed together at the fingertips.

"No, I haven't," admitted Chris, "Is it a play?"

"Ha!" exclaimed Gerry, raising his heavy-lidded eyes to the ceiling. Startled customers stared over at him, and he savoured the attention, then enlightened his friend. "Pray, Christopher, the fourth wall is not a play, but a method of acting."

"Oh, that Stanislavski thing," said Chris, unwrapping a sugar cube.

"No, not *that Stanislavski thing* at all, this is something quite different," said Gerry. "I was acting once, in a Welsh theatre. It was a scene from *A Midsummer Night's Dream*, and I was playing Nick Bottom. I was reciting that line: 'This is to make an ass of me, to fright me if they could,' when suddenly, the audience faded into the blackness, and in their place, there appeared the moonlit forest were the play is set. That forest was in front of me, behind me and in the wings of the theatre; created by my pure belief. I could see it. They call it the fourth wall. The first wall is the backdrop, the second and third walls are the entrances at the sides of the stage, and the fourth one is the one that appears downstage in the actor's mind," Gerry placed his index finger against his forehead. "I imagine Olivier has seen it."

"You're bonkers," Chris shrugged, "That's too deep, that. Now, let's get back to basics. Do you think we should write our own references and then send them to the Everyman?"

Gerry shook his head, "No, you tried that with the Playhouse if you recall … the forged reference from Sir Michael Redgrave, full of grammatical errors. They could have sued you for that."

"Then maybe we should just give up," said Chris sulkily.

Gerry grabbed his hand and squeezed, "Christopher, don't ever say those words."

"Get off!" Chris withdrew his hand and looked about the café at the disapproving glances.

"I thought we agreed we should never, ever ... under any circumstances ... give up our dreams?" said Gerry, reminding him of their personal manifesto.

"Yes, I know ... but ..."

Gerry traced the row of neon letters in the air with his finger and thumb: "'Tonight at the Old Vic – Christopher Anthony and Gerry Montague in *Death of a Salesman*!'"

"Oh, be quiet, Gerry," Chris told his histrionic friend. The waitress he was fond of was looking over, grinning at Gerry's antics and he felt embarrassed.

"Anyway," Gerry said, taking a delicate sip of coffee. "Are we still staying at your Aunt Gwendolen's place tonight?"

"No, we are not," replied Chris. "I'm not staying with the old bag. Her habits with her dentures disgust me and she never stops talking. I can't rehearse in those surroundings."

"Then we'd better start looking for digs soon, even if it means squatting," said Gerry. He folded his napkin into a triangle and ostentatiously dabbed at his face. Slight traces of foundation adhered to the tissue.

"I'm not squatting anywhere, I'm going home tonight," Chris said, his voice full of guilt and unable to look his friend in the eyes.

"Don't you have any spirit of adventure?" Gerry crumpled the napkin in his fist. "You're twenty-five years of age and living with your mum and dad in suburbia."

"Mossley Hill isn't that suburban," said Chris, apologetically.

"Middle class, suburban, square and grey ... my definition of Hell. Mossley Hell!" ranted Gerry, rather pleased with his own joke.

"Can you keep the noise down there, please?" said the waitress looking straight at Gerry.

Gerry stood up, donned his out-of-season mackintosh and beret and stormed towards the door, declaring, "Nevermore shall I seek refreshment in this dreadful establishment!" and with that he flounced off.

"Erm ... I'm sorry about this," Chris said to the waitress, who luckily saw the funny side of it all.

Gerry Montague marched off up Bold Street with Chris trotting after him. When Chris caught up with him, he was surprised to see that his friend had tears welling up in his eyes.

"Gerry, what's wrong?"

Gerry turned away and couldn't, or wouldn't answer. He increased his pace

115

and crossed Berry Street, continued up Bold Place, and as he tried to make the turning into Roscoe Street, Chris seized him by the lapels of his raincoat and pinned him against the wall.

"Look! I'm not your keeper, Gerry," he said, with a wild look in his eyes. "I can't take you home ... because ... because ... well ...you're homosexual, and they don't understand you. If my parents were different, of course you could stay with me in my room – obviously in separate beds because I'm not that way inclined."

Gerry started to laugh, and brushed away his tears.

"You're so square sometimes,' he said. "Anyway, I have to find a roof over my head for tonight, and I think I know just the place."

The two aspiring actors crossed the road and came to a backyard door with flaking black paint. With his usual, over-exaggerated, theatrical mannerisms Gerry looked both ways, and finding the coast was clear, lifted the door-latch and went into the yard, closely followed by Chris. They crossed the yard and Chris looked with dismay at the grimy panes of the ground-floor, net-curtained windows. Gerry climbed up four steps to a door, where he suddenly pulled out an old, long, rust-coloured key. He claimed it was a skeleton key that he had used many times in the past, yet as much as he rattled it about in the keyhole, nothing happened. The door simply refused to budge.

"Does anyone live here?' Chris asked, looking up at the two floors of windows.

Gerry shook his head. "Not in this flat, it's been empty for over a week. I've been reconnoitring ... blast! The lock almost yielded then."

"Are you sure the place is empty?" Chris asked, watching his friend's vain attempts to open the door.

"Yes! I am sure!" snarled Gerry, and he took out the alleged skeleton key and noticed that its shaft was slightly bent.

"Move out of the way," Chris said, calmly.

"I beg your pardon," said Gerry.

"I'll boot it open. Stand back!"

"You'll hurt yourself. It looks like a tough door," Gerry warned him and quickly skipped down the steps, out of harm's way.

Chris booted the door once, and cried out in pain.

"Break a leg," quipped Gerry.

In a rage, Chris kicked out once more and the sole of his shoe slammed into the door. It flew open.

"Bravo!"

Gerry applauded his friend and the two men crept gingerly into the flat, which had a tastefully furnished lounge, a kitchen, bathroom and two bedrooms. Gerry rooted about in the drawers of a sideboard and skimmed through several letters and bills addressed to a Michael Pagan.

Chris and Gerry stayed at the flat for a few days, living in mortal fear of Mr Pagan returning to his Roscoe Street abode. On the third day, at ten o'clock in the morning, the telephone started to ring. Gerry emerged from the bathroom with his face lathered in shaving foam. He stared in horror at the ringing telephone.

"Shall I answer it?" Chris wondered out loud.

Gerry swore in exasperation and told him to ignore it.

The phone rang for over a minute but it seemed like an eternity to the two men. About ten minutes later it started to ring once more, and this time it kept on ringing.

"This is getting on my nerves," snapped Chris, picking up the receiver, as Gerry gritted his teeth and waved his fist at him.

"Hello?" came a woman's voice.

"Hello," replied Chris.

"Is Michael Pagan still living there? Somebody told me that he'd died," said the caller. "Is that right?"

"I'm his brother Chris," said Chris, for some reason. "Can I help you?"

"Is your brother dead?"

"Yes, I'm afraid so … heart attack."

Gerry closed his eyes and shook his head slowly.

"Oh! I thought he'd died in a car crash."

Chris thought fast.

"Yes … yes he did … he was driving when he had the heart attack. Terrible affair. Who are you anyway?"

"My name's Melanie; I've used your brother before," she said.

At this, even Chris was baffled. Gerry put his ear close to the telephone earpiece and tried to eavesdrop.

"I seem to recall that Michael mentioned that he had a brother who was also a private detective," said Melanie. "Is that you?"

"Yes," said Chris, flatly. "I'm continuing his business. It's what he would have wanted, I know."

"In that case, would you be interested in taking on a case for me?" enquired the woman.

"What type of case?" asked Chris, intrigued.

"Oh, the usual thing ... terribly boring, I'm afraid ... I think my husband is seeing someone else, and I'd like you to find out who she is," said Melanie. "Would that be possible? I know it's still only a short time since ... er ..."

She sounded hurt, despite her attempt at flippancy.

"Okay, sounds straightforward enough. Where are you?"

Melanie gave a Childwall address, and then she added, "And will you be charging the same fee as your late brother? One hundred pounds a week, plus expenses?"

"Yes," Chris said, automatically. "That sounds about right," and a radiant smile broke out on his face.

"Could you call round tonight, say at about eight o' clock? My husband goes to his bridge club tonight, so he'll definitely be out at that time."

"Mm, let me just check my diary, Melanie," said the cheeky student, winking at his friend. "Let me see. Yes, eight o'clock will be fine. I'll see you then," and with that Melanie hung up.

"Well, you deserve an Oscar for that performance," said Gerry, with a frown on his face. "You don't know the first thing about the work of a private inquiry agent! You're going to get yourself into real trouble.

Chris couldn't take his friend seriously, partly because of the shaving foam dotted about his face, but mostly because of that one hundred pounds, plus expenses, that Melanie had promised.

"What's that quote you're always coming out with? 'The play's the thing'? Well I'm an actor, and in my humble opinion, not a bad one at that! I can certainly act the part of being a private eye. Chicken's feed! One hundred pounds! We could make a serious living out of this."

Chris could already visualise the fine suits, the fast cars, not to mention the exciting cases to solve.

"You're not living in the real world I'm afraid, Mr Anthony!" bawled Gerry. "Don't you think that the relatives of the late Mr Pagan just might turn up here soon to find out what they've inherited? And what will you do then, hey? How are you going to act your way out of that one?"

"Easy, we'll leave this place as soon as we get enough money," Chris assured him. "We'll rent an office on Dale Street, or somewhere, with a gold lettered sign in the window. It'll say, 'Anthony and Montague Investigations'. Yeah! no problem. Let's do it!"

"Such stuff as dreams are made on! You're a dreamer, Chris," said Gerry, returning to the bathroom to finish his shave.

"Hang on a minute, I thought you were the one who said we should never, ever, under any circumstances, give up our dreams?" Chris shouted after him. "Am I right?"

At 8pm that night, at the end of a long bus drive from the city centre, Chris and Gerry arrived at Melanie's house off Childwall Priory Road. She came to the door, a beautiful red-haired woman in her thirties with a pallid complexion and a pair of the most expressive blue eyes that Chris had ever seen. This was getting better and better. Chris introduced Gerry as his partner in the business, and all three settled down in the lounge around a coffee table, where Melanie gave the full details of the matter at hand.

"My husband, Cliff, is a company director of a business in Widnes. He's much older than me, but the age gap has never really bothered us, and no one has ever commented on it. He's a kind and loving person, and as far as I know, he's never been unfaithful to me in the five years we've been married, but for the past few months he's been staying out late, and I'm worried that there might be someone else."

"Staying out late!" Chris repeated, and scribbled the three words down in his notebook.

Gerry cringed at the sight of him doing that. He himself had a photographic memory, and could memorise an entire script after just one skim reading.

"Yes, he usually comes home from work at about six thirty, but on four occasions over the last two months he hasn't come back until one in the morning. Each time he's looked exhausted, and he's used various excuses to explain why he was late in coming home. He said he was working late once, but when I checked with his secretary, she told me that he'd left his office at half past five," Melanie told the men, and watched Chris trying to write it all down in the tiny notebook.

"What does your female intuition tell you, madam?" Gerry suddenly asked in an almost operatic voice. He stood up and squinted closely at the wedding photograph on the mantelpiece. "Ah, so this is your husband then?" he said, stating the obvious.

"Yes, I have some more recent photographs of him if you'd like to see them," said Melanie.

"Yes, in a while, but you never answered my first question," said Gerry, turning to face her.

Chris was annoyed by the way his friend was interfering with this first case –
trying to take over, as usual.

"Oh, well, I don't really know," said Melanie, awkwardly. "I mean, Cliff has
never even so much as looked at a woman besides me in our five years of
marriage."

"There's always a first time," said Chris, rather unhelpfully.

"You will need to supply me with the registration number of your husband's
car, and a list of the places in which he socialises," Gerry announced. In his
mind he was now no less a personage than Sherlock Holmes.

"I was just going to get to that, Gerry," said Chris, peeved.

Trying to look important, he began to consult the notes he had made in his
little black book.

Melanie gave them the address of her husband's office, his car registration
number, and a list of the clubs and two main pubs he occasionally visited. She
then paid Chris the one hundred pounds up front.

Chris and Gerry left their 'client's' house at 8.25pm and took a taxi to the
club in Longview where Cliff was supposedly playing bridge. The taxi drew into
the club car park at a quarter to nine, and as Chris was squabbling over the
amount the cabby was charging him, Cliff came out of the club with two men.
They got into an American Pontiac GTO.

Recognising their suspect from his photograph, Chris turned to the cabby and
said, "Wait a minute, mate. Follow that car."

"Are you kidding?" said the flat-capped world-weary driver. "This isn't the
movies you know."

"No, I'm not kidding. Follow it," Chris insisted.

"The game's afoot!" said Gerry, already entering the cab.

The Pontiac swung out of the car park with the hackney cab following at a
distance of about sixty yards.

"Don't get so close, mate," Chris told the driver. "They'll see us."

"Who are you following anyway?" the cabby wanted to know.

"It's confidential," Chris replied, trying to sound as enigmatic and
professional as possible.

"You'd better not be messing me about, son," the cabby warned, "because if
you don't pay up, and this is some kind of joke, I'll have the law on you, and
I've got three sons who'll make mincemeat of you as well!"

"Oh, please, just follow that car," Chris sighed and turned to Gerry, who was watching the Pontiac through the taxi's windscreen. "Do you think he knows we're following him?"

He nodded, and directed the cabby. "Driver, will you please decelerate and try your utmost to maintain a low profile?"

The Pontiac was travelling northwards towards Knowsley via a series of winding country roads and at one point, it slowed to negotiate a cinder track. At which point the taxi driver had had enough, and he turned off his lights and pulled the car to a halt under a clump of sycamores.

"Look, lads, what's going on? I'm not going any further," the driver told Chris and Gerry.

"We're private detectives," Chris said, his attention on the Pontiac which was crawling across the field towards a secluded country house.

"Pull the other one, it's got bells on," laughed the cabby.

Gerry left the taxi and Chris climbed out by the other door. He duly paid his fare, and the taxi driver promised to wait for "fifteen minutes tops". The amateur private detectives watched the Pontiac pull up at the house, and once they were sure that the three figures had gone into the dwelling, they walked slowly across the dark field towards it. Gerry cautiously moved over to the illuminated ground floor window and peeped through one of the panes. He could see several individuals dressed in smart three-piece suits, but no sign of Cliff, the man he was supposed to be watching.

Chris joined him at the window and looked in too. The two men then proceeded to the next window, which lit a room in which a chandelier burned brightly, but there was no one in that room.

"Don't move!" commanded a voice behind the amateur sleuths.

Chris turned first, to see the smartly attired elderly man standing with the huge white moustache. He was pointing a double-barrelled shotgun at his face. Another man arrived and stood beside the shotgun-toting stranger. It was Cliff – Melanie's husband.

"What are you doing here? Who sent you?" he asked the two trembling actors, as he herded them back across the lawn and away from the house with the gun.

"Drake, I bet," said the man with the shotgun.

"Nobody sent us, I'm looking for a relative," said Gerry, trying his utmost to smile and look natural.

"Don't take me for a fool," said the old man with the twenty-eight-inch-long, double-barrelled gun. "Show your chests."

Gerry and Chris looked at one another baffled.

"Now!" he screamed, as the heavy-moustachioed man's shotgun clicked.

Gerry obediently undid his coat and then lifted his jersey to reveal his pale and almost concave hairless chest. Chris, too, realised that this was not the time for questions and quickly undid the buttons of his shirt and bared his hairy pigeon chest as he gazed down the double barrels.

Cliff and the gunman scrutinised the hapless duo's chests, as if they expected to find some identifying marks or tattoos.

Seeing that such marks were not there, Cliff snapped, "So, you're not from Drake. Are you burglars then?"

"No, we're not," said Chris.

"No," said Gerry, simultaneously.

The ground suddenly shook and the whole country house swayed alarmingly, as if an earthquake had just struck. Through the windows, Chris and Gerry could see the chandeliers swinging wildly from the jolt.

"Get away from here now. Go on, clear off!" barked the man with the shotgun, and he and Cliff ran back towards the house.

Gerry and Chris were walking away, when Gerry's curiosity got the better of him, and he turned to see that the two men hurrying into the house had left the door ajar.

"Let's go and see what's going on," Gerry whispered, and started to tiptoe his way back towards the grand residence.

"Not on your Nellie, you idiot," hissed Chris. "What part of that double-barrelled shotgun did you not understand?" and he remained rooted to the spot fastening up his shirt.

"Very well, I'll go alone if you lack the nerve for it," said Gerry, with his usual melodramatic flair. "Call yourself a private detective!" and with that he crouched low and moved back towards the house.

"Damn you Gerry!"

Chris cursed the night air, then reluctantly followed his friend. The out-of-work actors sneaked into a long, oak-panelled hall with chequered floor tiles and then peeked into the large, elegantly furnished drawing room – but found it abandoned.

The house shook again, and this time an uproar of voices was heard after the tremor, and the noises seem to come from below. Chris and Gerry wandered into another room off the hallway and saw that a large red carpet had been rolled back to reveal an open floor hatch. The young men looked down into this hatch and saw stone steps leading down into what was presumably a cellar. The sounds of raised and excited voices were coming from down there.

"Let's get out of here, Gerry," whispered Chris.

"We're supposed to be detectives! Now come on!" Gerry wrenched his arm away from Chris's grip and descended the steps.

Chris reluctantly followed Gerry at what he thought was a safe distance, and they found themselves walking down a winding stone staircase into a long arched cellar lit by small, low-wattage bulbs. At the end of this cellar the two intrepid investigators came upon a huge vault, where a surreal and terrifying scene met their eyes.

Five men in long black robes and pointed hoods were chanting incomprehensible words as they presented their palms to something grotesque and amorphous that seemed to be hovering close to the floor some thirty feet away from them. The unidentified thing resembled a giant sea anemone, about six feet across, with a rim of writhing, squirming green tentacles and a huge yellow eye in its centre. Cliff and the man with the white moustache stood with their backs to Chris and Gerry, intently watching this absurd-looking but terrifying creature. The man with the shotgun suddenly raised his weapon, pointed it at the tentacled monstrosity and discharged two barrels. The creature's large yellow eye merely blinked at the combined blasts, it made a repulsive hissing sound and extended a tentacle at the old man, who reacted by backing away and bumping into Cliff.

Chris found himself scrambling up the stone steps with Gerry in hot pursuit. The two men fled straight out of the house and across the field where, to their utter relief, the taxi driver was still waiting in his cab. Chris and Gerry urged him to make a quick getaway, so he started the hackney cab, and with a screech of tyres reversed back up the lane and on to Liverpool.

Gerry and Chris both agreed that it might be wise to leave the flat on Roscoe Street. Chris went to live with his parents for a while, and Gerry booked a room at Hunt's Hotel on Mount Pleasant for a week to recover from his shattering ordeal. Gerry wrote a letter to Cliff's wife, telling her what had happened that night, even though he was sure she wouldn't believe him, he thought it was the least he could do, and might perhaps throw some light on why her husband was staying out late each week. Gerry and Chris had no idea what they had witnessed, but they instinctively felt that it had something to do with the occult.

When I heard of their story, many years later, I was able to explain to them exactly what had happened, and now I will tell you too.

The house up in Knowsley was the meeting place for a lodge of magicians. When I say magicians, I do not mean the slight-of hand entertainers who pull rabbits out of hats, but actual practitioners of real magic, or warlocks, to use the proper terminology.

In 1966, a rival lodge of extreme black magic practitioners was founded by an occultist by the name of Drake at a house just over a mile away from the one in Knowsley, and the members of this new lodge declared war on the warlocks whom they saw as adversaries. Animal, and possibly human sacrifices were made with the intention of conjuring up long-buried malevolent forces deep beneath the earth. One of these ancient evil spirits – known as the Mox – was specifically conjured up by Drake's warlocks and directed towards the Knowsley lodge, and it periodically emerged from the bowels of the earth to wreak havoc in the great vault excavated beneath the house as a meeting place for the magicians. This horrifying antediluvian entity is said to have killed three of the magicians at the Knowsley lodge, until it finally turned on Drake and the extreme Satanic lodge members who had first awakened it, and it destroyed them all. The house of this rival lodge was burnt to the ground by a fire of unknown origin, and not a trace of a single body was ever found within its smouldering ruins.

TWO STRANGE TALES

People often ask me what the strangest stories are that I've investigated over the years, and it is rather difficult to answer, as most of the incidents I've looked into in the past have been rather unusual, to say the least; however, the following two episodes have stuck in my mind.

In May 1982, twenty-year-old Andrew Connolly was living off Park Road North, in Birkenhead. Picking up his mail from his doormat one morning, he groaned as he saw the usual collection of bills and junk mail. Among the mail was a very curious manila envelope which bore a stamp of Adolf Hitler in profile. It struck Andrew immediately that Hitler was a rather distasteful subject to be featured on a British stamp, and he also noted that although the franking mark stated that the letter had been posted in Liverpool, it also bore a swastika and the German word 'Postzustellung' – which means service by mail.

On opening the envelope, Andrew saw that the letter it contained was signed by his friend in Liverpool, John Hughes, who lived in Toxteth, but the subject of the letter was bizarre. John stated that he was about to be transported to a Welsh mine to drill for a newly-discovered ore for the 'Power Centre of Island Station One'. The letter went on to say that historical monuments in Liverpool were being dismantled and that Lime Street was being renamed Goethe Strasse.

On the following day Andrew travelled over to Liverpool and showed his friend John the strange-looking letter with the stamp of Hitler upon it. John was as dumbfounded as Andrew, because he hadn't written such a letter, and certainly hadn't been party to any kind of hoax.

The conundrum was never solved, but it made me wonder if that letter had crossed over from another dimension – an alternative universe where perhaps Hitler won WWII and renamed Britain as Island Station One. Perhaps for a brief instant, the dimensions of our world overlapped the dimensions of a world where history turned out differently, and through that wafer-thin partition came an envelope from a Britain conquered by the Nazis. A philatelist looked at the Hitler stamp and declared it to be a genuine factory-standard print, which deepens the mystery even further.

***

Coincidences also fascinate me, and make me wonder if some intelligence – some cosmic joker, if you like – is pulling the strings somewhere up there. A case in point is the incident which took place in the 1980s on Church Street. Roger and Gina, a couple in their thirties, had divorced, and Gina had taken custody of their only child, four-year-old Daniel. Mother and son had moved from their home in Chester after an acrimonious divorce to live with relatives in Woolton, and Roger missed his son so much that he had turned to drink.

Six months after the divorce, in April 1984, Gina and Daniel were out shopping on Liverpool's Church Street, when a heart-stopping incident took place. Two teenaged yobs cut the thick nylon cord holding up dozens of giant novelty helium balloons at a temporary stall, and as the balloons shot upwards, their strings caught young Daniel under his arm. The boy dangled from the balloons as they soared high above the milling crowds of shoppers, and Gina screamed and chased after her son, who was starting to sob. The balloons reached the corner of Whitechapel, chased by an anxious crowd. All of a sudden, the handle of someone's umbrella was thrust upwards, and it caught the mass of strings, but dragged the man holding the brolly along the ground for some twenty feet. The little child was then extricated from the tangled lines, and his rescuer walked to Gina carrying the tearful boy. The rescuer turned out to be none other than Roger, the boy's father, who just happened to be in Liverpool that day.

The couple embraced, and then went for a coffee. It seems that the incredible coincidence reunited them, because they remarried that summer.

OTHER TITLES BY TOM SLEMEN

HAUNTED LIVERPOOL 1	Tom Slemen	£5.99
HAUNTED LIVERPOOL 2	Tom Slemen	£5.99
HAUNTED LIVERPOOL 3	Tom Slemen	£5.99
HAUNTED LIVERPOOL 4	Tom Slemen	£5.99
HAUNTED LIVERPOOL 5	Tom Slemen	£5.99
HAUNTED LIVERPOOL 6	Tom Slemen	£5.99
HAUNTED LIVERPOOL 7	Tom Slemen	£5.99
HAUNTED LIVERPOOL 8	Tom Slemen	£5.99
HAUNTED LIVERPOOL 9	Tom Slemen	£5.99
HAUNTED LIVERPOOL 10	Tom Slemen	£5.99
HAUNTED LIVERPOOL 11	Tom Slemen	£5.99
HAUNTED LIVERPOOL 12	Tom Slemen	£5.99
HAUNTED LIVERPOOL ANTHOLOGY	Tom Slemen	£6.99
STRANGE LIVERPOOL	Tom Slemen	£5.99
HAUNTED WIRRAL	Tom Slemen	£5.99
LIVERPOOL GHOST WALK	Tom Slemen	£5.99
HAUNTED CHESHIRE	Tom Slemen	£5.99
WICKED LIVERPOOL	Tom Slemen	£5.99
HAUNTED LIVERPOOL double cassette and audio book read by	Tom Slemen	£8.99

Available from all good bookshops
For a free stocklist contact:
The Bluecoat Press
19 Rodney Street
Liverpool L1 9EF
Telephone: 0151 707 2390
Website: www.bluecoatpress.co.uk

If you have had a paranormal encounter, or a supernatural experience of any sort, please drop a line to Tom Slemen c/o the above address.